PRIMARY MATHEMATICS

Challenging
Word Problems

SINGAPORE MATH® PROGRAM

Yan Kow Cheong

Marshall Cavendish Education

This edition ©2014 Marshall Cavendish Education Pte Ltd

Published by Marshall Cavendish Education
Times Centre, 1 New Industrial Road, Singapore 536196
Customer Service Hotline: (65) 6213 9688
US Office Tel: (+1-914) 332 8888 | Fax: (+1-914) 332 8882
E-mail: cs@mceducation.com
Website: www.mceducation.com

First published 2010
New edition 2014
Reprinted 2014, 2015, 2017, 2018 (twice), 2019, 2020 (twice), 2021

Primary Mathematics (Common Core Edition) Challenging Word Problems 2
ISBN 978-981-01-8972-3

Printed in Singapore

We would like to acknowledge contributions by:

Primary Mathematics (Common Core Edition) Challenging Word Problems
Jennifer Kempe (Curriculum Advisor from Singapore Math Inc.®)

Preface

 **Common Core Edition** **Challenging Word Problems** provides graded exercises for students of mixed abilities and challenging questions for better math students. This series is written to supplement Singapore's **Primary Mathematics** textbooks (Common Core Edition) distributed by Singapore Math Inc.® for use in the USA.

Adopting a topical approach in which mathematical concepts and skills are taught and reinforced, the **Challenging Word Problems** series serves to improve students' problem-solving skills and enhance their mathematical reasoning.

Each book in the series features the following:

- **Worked Examples** for each topic show common methods of solution used in the Primary Mathematics textbooks;

- **Practice Questions** allow students to apply and practice questions similar to the ones discussed in the Worked Examples and in the Primary Mathematics textbooks;

- **Challenging Problems** provide opportunities for more capable students to solve higher-order word problems and further develop their problem-solving skills;

- **Review Questions** allow students to test their understanding of the concepts discussed in earlier topics and in the Primary Mathematics textbooks;

- **Answers** allow teachers or students to check their answers to all practice exercises and challenging problems;

- **Worked solutions** provide commonly used methods of solving non-routine questions, while encouraging creative or intuitive ones as well.

A student's guide to using the **Challenging Word Problems** series effectively.

1. Read each question given in the Worked Example. Try to solve it before reading the solution.

2. If your solution is similar to the one given in the Worked Example, well done. If you have used a different method, yet have arrived at the same answer, great—you now have at least two methods of solving this question.

3. If your answer is different, look at your work again and figure out where you may have gone wrong.

4. If you have understood all the worked examples, proceed to the Practice Questions; then check your answers with the ones at the back of the book. Should you get stuck at any question, don't panic; go through it again. If you still find difficulty in solving the question, seek help from your friend or teacher.

5. If you have understood and solved all the Practice Questions, you are now ready to try the Challenging Problems. Do them on your own first. Seek help only if you need some hints or clarification.

6. Try to come up with similar questions and challenge your friends to solve them. For a given question, discuss some possible solutions that you may have used in arriving at the answer.

Contents

1 Addition and Subtraction

Worked Example 1

A cruise ship with 218 passengers on board picked up another 185 passengers at the next port. How many passengers are on board now?

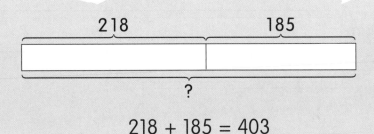

218   185

?

$$218 + 185 = 403$$

403 passengers are on board now.

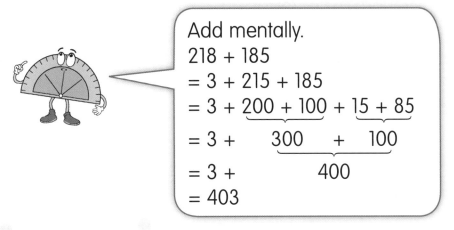

Add mentally.
218 + 185
= 3 + 215 + 185
= 3 + 200 + 100 + 15 + 85
= 3 + 300 + 100
= 3 + 400
= 403

Worked Example 2

Pam has 138 magazines.
Pete has 59 fewer magazines than Pam.
(a) How many magazines does Pete have?
(b) How many magazines do they have altogether?

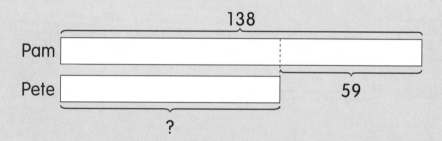

(a) 138 − 59 = 79
   Pete has **79** magazines.

(b) 138 + 79 = 217
   They have **217** magazines altogether.

Think: How would the answer change if Pam has 59 fewer magazines than Pete instead? Would the total number of magazines remain unchanged?

Practice Questions

Answer each question carefully. Show your work and write your statement clearly.

1. Mr. Smith sold 180 apples. Mr. Brown sold 70 more apples than Mr. Smith. How many apples did Mr. Brown sell?

2. A street vendor sold 265 hotdogs on Saturday and 348 hotdogs on Sunday. How many hotdogs did he sell on the 2 days?

3. The Hamilton family has a total of 600 sheep and cows on their farm. There are 348 sheep. How many cows are there?

4. At a math workshop, 425 out of 752 who attended were women. How many men attended the workshop?

5. In the beginning, there were 824 students at a public library. After 2 hours, 505 students remained. How many students left the library?

6. After selling 135 bananas, Mr. Greg still had 265 bananas left. How many bananas did he have at first?

7. Troy read 314 magazines. Mike also read some magazines. If Mike had read 68 fewer magazines, he would have read the same number of magazines as Troy.
   (a) How many magazines did Mike read?
   (b) How many magazines did they read altogether?

8. Belinda has 409 ribbons. If she gives away 238 ribbons, she will have the same number of ribbons as June.
   (a) How many ribbons does June have?
   (b) How many ribbons do they have altogether?

9. Hall A can seat 426 people and Hall B can seat 567 people. How many people can both halls seat altogether?

10. In a science quiz, Willie scored 857 points and Zac scored 168 fewer points than Willie. How many points did Zac score?

Challenging Problems

Worked Example 1

Josie had 243 ribbons. After giving away 78 ribbons, she had the same number of ribbons as Kelly. How many ribbons do they have in all now?

```
                     243
       ┌─────────────────────┬─────────┐
Josie  │                     ┊         │
       └─────────────────────┴─────────┘
       ┌─────────────────────┐    78
Kelly  │                     │
       └─────────────────────┘
              ?
```

$$243 - 78 = 165$$

Kelly has **165** ribbons.

```
                    165
         ┌─────────────────────┐
Josie    │                     │
         └─────────────────────┘
         ┌─────────────────────┐
Kelly    │                     │
         └─────────────────────┘
                    165
```

$$165 + 165 = 330$$

They have **330** ribbons in all now.

Worked Example 2

Susan started to read her book in order from page 107 up to a certain page. If the total number of pages she read was 210, what was the last page she read?

Method 1

Page 107 ——————————————— Page ◯

⌣ 210 pages

◻ − 107 + 1 = 210

◻ − 106 = 210

◻ = 210 + 106

= 316

From pages 10 to 17, there are 17 − 10 + 1 = 8 pages.

The last page she read was **316**.

Method 2

210 + 107 − 1 = 316

The last page she read was **316**.

Do these problems. Show your work and write your statements clearly.

1. Team A scored 247 points. Team A scored 162 fewer points than team B. Team B scored 107 fewer points than team C. How many points did team C score?

2. Cally and Karen have a total of 303 cards. Karen has 187 cards. If Cally gives away 47 cards, how many cards does she have now?

3. Phil has 192 toy cars. George has 26 more toy cars than Phil but 83 fewer toy cars than Eric. How many toy cars does Eric have?

4. Sandy drew 80 drawings. Lily drew 17 fewer drawings than Sandy. How many drawings did they draw in all?

5. On a train, 308 passengers were seated and 127 passengers were standing. At the second station, 52 people left the train and 147 people boarded the train. How many passengers were on board after the second station?

6. In a contest, Sam scored 101 points. Fiona scored 25 points short of 120 points. How many points did they score in all?

7. Veronica read from page 123 to page 160 of an encyclopedia. Then she started reading in order again from page 202 up to a certain page. If the total number of pages she read was 76, at what page did she stop reading?

8. Faith and Annie have 520 beads altogether. Faith has 230 beads. If Annie loses 74 beads, how many beads does she have left?

9. Jason has 51 buttons. 19 of them are red and 17 are green. The rest of his buttons are blue. How many more red than blue buttons does he have?

10. Alicia has 161 fewer ribbons than Manny. Manny has 520 ribbons. How many ribbons do they have altogether?

2 Length

Worked Example 1

John cut 178 cm of string to tie a gift. He still had 57 cm of string left. What was the original length of the string?

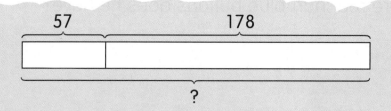

57	178

?

$$57 + 178 = 235$$

The original length of the string was **235 cm**.

Worked Example 2

Pete is 170 cm tall. Wendy is 23 cm shorter than Pete.
(a) How tall is Wendy?
(b) What is the total height of Pete and Wendy?

(a)

170

Pete

Wendy   23

?

$$170 - 23 = 147$$

Wendy is **147 cm** tall.

(b)

170

Pete

Wendy   ?

147

$$170 + 147 = 317$$

The total height of Pete and Wendy is **317 cm**.

or

$$170 + 170 - 23 = 317$$

Note: There is no need to know the height of Wendy to find the total height.

Practice Questions

Answer each question carefully. Show your work and write your statement clearly.

1. Benjamin is 174 cm tall. His sister is 37 cm shorter than him. How tall is Benjamin's sister?

2. The total length of two ropes is 143 cm. If the shorter rope is 68 cm, find the length of the longer rope.

3. Stick M is 105 cm long. Stick N is 67 cm longer than stick M. How long is stick N?

4. Agnes is 168 cm tall. Dave is 16 cm taller than Agnes.
   (a) How tall is Dave?
   (b) What is the total height of Agnes and Dave?

5. A black ant covered 182 cm in a given time. A red ant covered 37 cm less than the black ant in the same time. How far did the red ant cover in the given time?

6. The distance between shops P and Q is 358 yd. The distance between shops P and R is 754 yd. What is the distance between shops Q and R if shop Q lies between shop P and shop R?

7. Flynn walked 405 m to Theo's house. After meeting with Theo, Flynn walked another 398 m to his uncle's house. How far did Flynn walk altogether?

8. Two girls have a total height of 200 cm. One girl is 131 cm tall. How tall is the shorter girl?

9. After using 128 cm of ribbon to make a bow, there was 347 cm of ribbon left. What was the length of the ribbon at first?

10. Tom's school is 950 m away from his house. His aunt's house is 805 m away from his school. How much farther is Tom's school from his house than from his aunt's house?

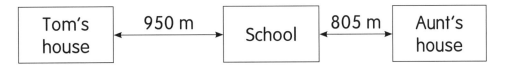

Challenging Problems

Worked Example 1

String A is 92 cm long. String B is 35 cm shorter than string A, and 17 cm shorter than string C. What is the length of string C?

Method 1

92

String A

String B   35

String C

17

?

$$92 - 35 = 57$$

String B is 57 cm long.

$$57 + 17 = 74$$

The length of string C is **74 cm**.

Method 2

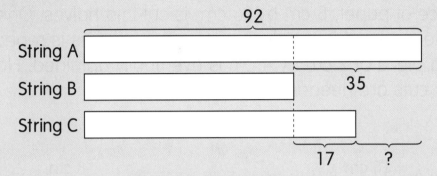

$$35 - 17 = 18$$

String A is 18 cm longer than string C.

$$92 - 18 = 74$$

The length of string C is **74 cm**.

Worked Example 2

A piece of paper, 8 cm by 16 cm, is cut into halves. One of the pieces is cut into halves again. The process is repeated until a piece of 2 cm by 4 cm is eventually obtained. How many cuts are needed in all?

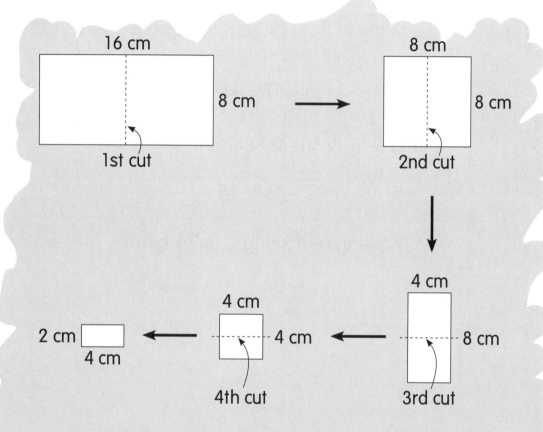

4 cuts are needed to obtain a piece of paper 2 cm by 4 cm.

Note: We could also use one unit instead of a rectangle.

Do these problems. Show your work and write your statements clearly.

1. Suzie jogged 218 m and then took a short rest. She then jogged another 168 m. She still has another 294 m to jog. When she finishes, how for will she have jogged?

2. When Bradley stands on a stool, the total height of him and the stool is 68 in. If the stool is 9 in., how much taller is Bradley than the stool?

3. Patty jogged 318 m from her home to the library. She then jogged another 205 m from the library to the stadium. Finally, she jogged the last 135 m from the stadium to her father's shop. How far did Patty jog in all?

4. Rope P is 78 ft long. Rope Q is 25 ft longer than rope P, but 24 ft shorter than rope R. What is the length of rope R?

5. String P is 121 in. long. String R is 29 in. shorter than string P. String Q is 38 in. longer than string R. How long is string Q?

6. One ribbon measures 78 cm, which is 23 cm shorter than another ribbon. What is the total length of both ribbons?

7. Rope A is 26 cm shorter than rope B. Rope C is 32 cm longer than rope B. If rope A is 85 cm long, what is the length of rope C?

8. Both Kate and Dianne are running in a 400-meter race. Kate is 120 m from the finishing line. Dianne is 30 m behind Kate.
   (a) How far away is Kate from the starting line?
   (b) How far away is Dianne from the starting line?

9. String P is 32 cm longer than string R. String Q is 15 cm longer than string R. String Q is 138 cm long. What is the length of string P?

10. An ant in a well wants to get out. The well is 6 m deep. Each day, the ant climbs up 4 m, but at night, it falls back 2 m. How many days will it take the ant to climb out of the well?

3 Multiplication and Division by 2 and 3

Worked Example 1

Helen has 8 books.
(a) Carol has twice as many books as Helen. How many books does Carol have?
(b) Veron has half as many books as Helen. How many books does Veron have?

(a)

$$8$$

Helen

Carol

?

$$2 \times 8 = 16$$

Carol has **16** books.

(b)

$$8$$

Helen

Veron

?

$$8 \div 2 = 4$$

Veron has **4** books.

Worked Example 2

Joel buys 18 books from a book fair.
(a) If he groups them equally on 2 shelves, how many books will there be on each shelf?
(b) If he groups them equally on 3 shelves, how many books will there be on each shelf?

(a)

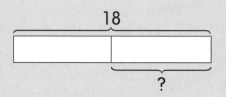

$18 \div 2 = 9$
There will be **9** books on each shelf.

(b)

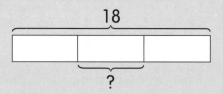

$18 \div 3 = 6$
There will be **6** books on each shelf.

Worked Example 3

Three stickers cost $1. Jerry bought 15 stickers in all. How much did he pay?

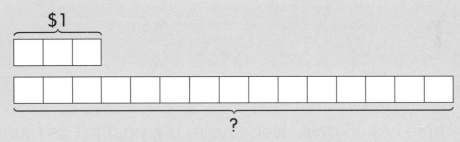

$1

?

1 group of 3 stickers costs $1.

$$15 \div 3 = 5$$

5 groups cost $5 \times \$1 = \$5$.

Jerry paid **$5** for the stickers.

Practice Questions

Answer each question carefully. Show your work and write your statement clearly.

1. Philip has 24 marbles. He wants to divide them in groups of 3. How many groups of marbles will he have?

2. Annie has 18 dolls. Her cousin, Lily, has half as many dolls as she does. How many dolls does Lily have?

3. A watch has 3 hands: the hour hand, the minute hand, and the second hand. Mr. Thomson has 4 such watches. How many hands do his watches have in all?

4. While sitting on a log in the forest, William and Kate saw 9 deer. How many ears do 9 deer have?

5. Dan has 8 cakes. Duke has 3 times as many cakes as Dan. How many cakes does Duke have?

6. Mr. and Mrs. Duncan went to see a concert with their child. Mr. Duncan paid $27 for their tickets. If each ticket costs the same, what was the price of one ticket?

7. Mr. Davies decides to divide his class of 20 girls and 10 boys into equal groups. Each group has 2 girls and 1 boy. How many groups can he form in all?

8. Every album has 10 photos. How many photos will 3 such albums have?

9. Mrs. O'Hara bought 12 pears. Three pears cost $1. How much did she pay?

10. Mr. Wilson sells bicycles in his shop. He counts 20 wheels in all. How many bicycles are there in his shop?

Challenging Problems

Worked Example 1

The distance between the first lamp post and the fourth lamp post is 12 m. If all the lamp posts are equally spaced, what is the distance from the fifth lamp post to the seventh lamp post?

12 m

❋   ❋   ❋   ❋
1st   2nd   3rd   4th

From the 1st lamp post to the 4th lamp post, there are 3 intervals. Each interval is 12 ÷ 3 = 4 m long.

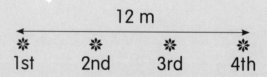

❋ 4 m ❋ 4 m ❋
5th   6th   7th

From the 5th lamp post to the 7th lamp post, there are 2 intervals.

$$2 \times 4 = 8$$

The distance from the 5th lamp post to the 7th lamp post is **8 m**.

Worked Example 2

Mandy bakes 4 cookies. Amy bakes 3 times as many cookies as Mandy. Amy bakes twice as many cookies as Kat. How many cookies does Kat bake?

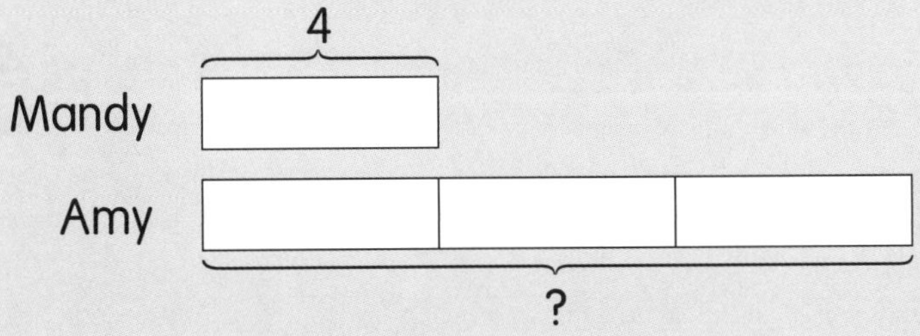

Mandy | 4

Amy | ?

$$3 \times 4 = 12$$

Amy bakes 12 cookies.

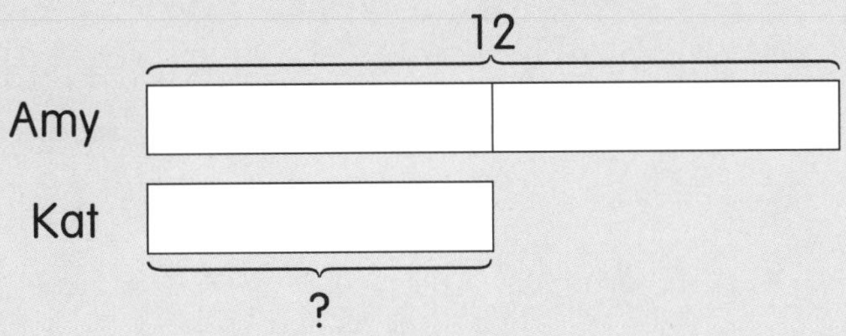

Amy | 12

Kat | ?

$$2 \text{ units} = 12$$

$$1 \text{ unit} = 12 \div 2 = 6$$

Kat bakes **6** cookies.

Do these problems. Show your work and write your statements clearly.

1. Mrs. Amy sewed some skirts. She used 3 big buttons and 2 small buttons for each skirt. If she used 15 big buttons altogether, how many small buttons did she use?

2. Trees are planted at an equal distance of 3 m away from each other along a road. If there are 6 trees along the road, how far is the last tree from the first tree?

3. A gardener is arranging plants in the garden. There are 24 plants altogether. If he arranges the plants in rows of 3, how many rows are there?

4. A mother rabbit and her 2 baby rabbits each eat 1 carrot a day. How many carrots will this rabbit family eat in 4 days?

5. Each time a juggler goes on stage, he increases the number of balls he juggles. He juggles 2 balls the first time. The second time, he juggles 4 balls. The third time, he juggles 6 balls. If this continues, how many balls will he juggle when he goes on stage the fifth time?

6. The distance between the first tree and the fourth tree along a straight road is 21 yd. What is the distance between two trees next to each other if the trees are equally spaced?

7. At a party, there were 7 children. There were 18 tarts on a plate. Each girl ate 2 tarts and each boy ate 3 tarts. All the tarts were eaten. How many girls were there at the party?

8. Agnes has fewer than 12 balloons. She can divide the balloons equally into 2 groups. She can also divide them equally into 3 groups. How many balloons does she have?

9. There are 6 lamp posts along a street. The lamp posts are 3 m apart from each other. How far is the sixth lamp post from the first lamp post?

10. Angie has 5 stamps. Paul has twice as many stamps as Angie. Doreen has 3 times as many stamps as Paul. How many stamps does Doreen have?

4 Mental Calculation

Worked Example 1

Add mentally.
(a) 46 + 38
(b) 19 + 43 + 21
(c) 37 + 14 + 63

(a) 46 + 38 = ?
46 + 30 = 76   38
76 + 8 = 80 + 4   / \
        = **84**   30   8
     / \
    4   4

Mentally add the tens first, then the ones.

(b) 19 + 43 + 21 = 19 + 21 + 43
                 = 40 + 43
                 = **83**

Look for pairs that make up 100.

(c) 37 + 14 + 63 = 37 + 63 + 14
                 = 100 + 14
                 = **114**

Worked Example 2

Subtract this mentally.
42 − 15

Method 1

42 − 15 = ?
42 − 10 = 32
32 − 5 = 25 + 2
     ⁄ ＼   = **27**
30   2

Subtract the tens first, then the ones.

Method 2

42 − 15 = 42 + 3 − 15 − 3
        = 45 − 15 − 3
        = 30 − 3
        = **27**

Adding 3 and subtracting 3 equals 0.

Method 3

42 − 15 = 42 − 12 − 3
        = 30 − 3
        = **27**

39

Worked Example 3

Calculate mentally.
(a) 367 + 99
(b) 482 − 98

(a) $367 + 99 = \underline{367 + 100} - 1$
   $= \quad 467 \quad - 1$
   $= \textbf{466}$

1 more than 99 is 100.

(b) $482 - 98 = \underline{482 - 100} + 2$
   $= \quad 382 \quad + 2$
   $= \textbf{384}$

2 more than 98 is 100.

Practice Questions

Answer each question carefully.

1. Add mentally.

    (a) 20 + 38 + 30

    (b) 57 + 36

    (c) 197 + 99

    (d) 83 + 22 + 97

2. Subtract mentally.

    (a) 52 − 39

    (b) 71 − 43

    (c) 401 − 95

    (d) 122 − 98

3. What number is 38 less than the total of 28 and 72?

4. The numbers of potted plants sold by a nursery in four days are 9, 10, 7, and 3. What is the total number of potted plants sold?

5. The numbers of stamps in three albums are 22, 44, and 56. What is the total number of stamps in the three albums?

6. The numbers of bottles of mineral water sold by a shop in three days are 47, 126, and 43. What is the total number of bottles of mineral water sold in three days?

7. At a fair, the numbers of coupons collected by three stalls are 82, 97, and 73. What is the total number of coupons collected?

8. Lawrence made 97 egg sandwiches. He made 49 fewer tuna sandwiches. How many tuna sandwiches did he make?

9. Edward has $98 less than Susan. Susan has $256. How much money does Edward have?

10. There are 97 oranges and some apples in a basket. There are 102 fruits in all. How many apples are there?

Challenging Problems

Worked Example 1

Add mentally.

(a) 69 + 24   (b) 48 + 25 + 18   (c) 316 + 57

(a) 69 + 24 = 69 + 1 + 23
            =   70   + 23
            = **93**

One number "gives" 1 to the other.

(b) 48 + 25 + 18
         ╱ ╲
        2   23

   = 48 + 2 + 23 + 18
              ╱ ╲
             1   22

   = 50 + 1 + 22 + 18
   = 50 + 1 +   40
   = **91**

One number "gives" 3 to the other.

(c) 316 + 57 = 313 + 3 + 57
             = 313 +   60
             = 373
             = **373**

Worked Example 2

Subtract mentally.

(a) 97 – 29   (b) 82 – 53   (c) 681 – 48

(a) 97 – 29 = 98 – 30
$\qquad$ = **68**

or

97 – 29 = $\underset{\smile}{97 - 27}$ – 2
$\qquad$ = 70 – 2
$\qquad$ = **68**

Increase both numbers by 1.

(b) $\qquad$ 82 – 53

79 + 3 50 + 3
= 79 – 50
= **29**

or

82 – 53 = $\underset{\smile}{82 - 52}$ – 1
$\qquad$ = 30 – 1
$\qquad$ = **29**

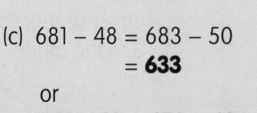

Subtract 3 from both numbers.

(c) 681 – 48 = 683 – 50
$\qquad$ = **633**

or

681 – 48 = $\underset{\smile}{678 - 48}$ + 3
$\qquad$ = 630 + 3
$\qquad$ = **633**

Increase both numbers by 2.

Do these problems.

1. Add mentally.
   (a) 68 + 25   (b) 59 + 39

2. Subtract mentally.
   (a) 88 – 39   (b) 73 – 34

3. Add mentally.
   (a) 138 + 29   (b) 423 + 48

4. Subtract mentally.
   (a) 183 – 57   (b) 753 – 29

5. Subtract 49 from the total of 163 and 97.

6. The numbers of buttons in four boxes are 39, 8, 28, and 22. What is the total number of buttons in the four boxes?

7. The numbers of eggs laid over two days in a chicken coop were 105 and 89. How many eggs were laid in all?

8. The numbers of hamsters sold by three pet shops are 59, 38, and 63. What is the total number of hamsters sold?

9. Catherine has 131 stickers which she put in two boxes. 43 stickers are in the first box and the rest are in the second box. How many stickers are in the second box?

10. A baker prepared 115 cookies and sold 78 of them. How many cookies were left?

Worked Example 1

David distributed 36 walnuts equally among 4 students.
(a) How many walnuts did each student get?
(b) How many walnuts did 3 students get altogether?

Method 1

(a) $36 \div 4 = 9$

Each student got **9** walnuts.

(b) $3 \times 9 = 27$

Three students got **27** walnuts altogether.

Method 2

(a) $36 = \underbrace{4 \times 9}$

4 groups of 9

Each student got **9** walnuts.

(b) 1 student got 9 walnuts.

3 students got $3 \times 9 = 27$ walnuts.

Three students got **27** walnuts altogether.

Worked Example 2

One bag of apples cost $1. There were 5 apples in one bag. Mary bought 35 apples in all. How much did Mary pay?

Method 1

$$35 \div 5 = 7$$

She bought 7 bags of apples.

$$7 \times \$1 = \$7$$

Mary paid **$7**.

Method 2

$$35 \text{ apples} = 5 \text{ apples} \times 7$$

There were 7 bags of apples.

1 bag of 5 apples cost $1.

7 bags of 35 apples cost $7 \times \$1 = \$7$.

Mary paid **$7**.

Worked Example 3

Yvonne has 5 necklaces. Each necklace has 3 green beads and 6 white beads. How many beads does Yvonne have in total?

$3 + 6 = 9$

Each necklace has 9 beads.

$5 \times 9 = 45$

Yvonne has **45** beads in total.

Practice Questions

Answer each question carefully. Show your work and write your statement clearly.

1. Each student needs 4 notebooks.
   (a) How many notebooks do 5 students need?
   (b) How many notebooks do 8 students need?

2. Mrs. Brandon buys 7 shirts for her nephews and nieces. Each shirt has 5 buttons. How many buttons are there altogether?

3. Mrs. Johnson distributed 80 books equally among 2 girls and 6 boys. How many books did each child receive?

4. There are 10 rose plants in Mrs. White's garden. There are 6 roses on each plant. How many roses are there altogether?

5. At a fruit stand, 5 oranges were sold for $3. Mr. Tomlin bought 30 oranges in all. How much did he pay?

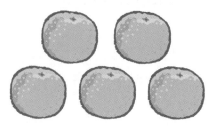

6. Sandra has 10 boxes of pens. Each box has 3 blue pens and 2 red pens. How many pens does she have altogether?

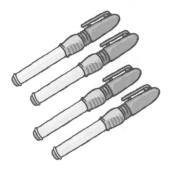

7. Irene has 4 necklaces. Each necklace has 3 red beads and 5 yellow beads. How many beads does she have in total?

8. There are 40 people going to a beach and a van can take only 8 people. How many vans will be needed to transport all the people?

9. A table can seat 9 students. How many tables are needed to seat 36 students?

10. Belinda and Charles have a total of 24 bookmarks. They decide to share them equally with Sheila and Harry. How many bookmarks will each person get?

Challenging Problems

Worked Example 1

Mr. Jacobs has 5 coins. His son, Arthur, has 7 times as many coins as he does. How many coins do they have in all?

Method 1

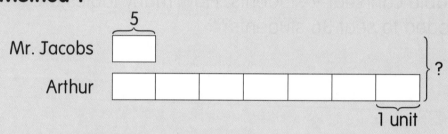

1 unit + 7 units = 8 units
1 unit = 5
8 units = 8 × 5
        = 40

They have **40** coins in all.

Method 2

1 unit = 5
7 units = 7 × 5 = 35

35 + 5 = 40

They have **40** coins in all.

Worked Example 2

Helen has 6 buttons. Nancy has 5 times as many buttons as Helen. Nancy has 3 times as many buttons as Tess.
(a) How many buttons does Nancy have?
(b) How many buttons does Tess have?

(a)
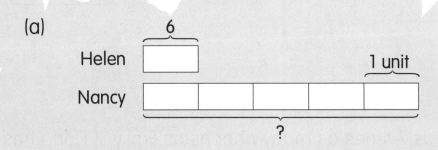

1 unit = 6
5 units = 5 × 6
= 30

Nancy has **30** buttons.

(b)

30

Nancy

Tess

?

3 units = 30
1 unit = 30 ÷ 3
= 10

Tess has **10** buttons.

Do these problems. Show your work and write your statements clearly.

1. Karam has 10 markers. Benjamin has 4 times as many markers as Karam. How many markers do they have in all?

2. Fiona has 7 times as many ribbons as Emily. If Fiona has 28 ribbons, how many more ribbons does Fiona have?

3. Stephanie lives on the sixth floor of a high-rise apartment. The staircase from one floor to the next has 10 steps. How many steps does she have to climb from the first floor to reach her home?

4. Judith and her 7 friends each had 2 lollipops and 3 strawberries. How many lollipops and strawberries were there altogether?

5. How many different answers can be formed by multiplying any two of the numbers on the card?

4   5
2   3

6. There are 24 students in Mr. Edmund's class.
   (a) If there are 6 students in each group, how many groups can be formed?
   (b) If there are 8 students in each group, how many groups can be formed?

7. Patrick wants to buy a toy plane. The toy plane costs $45. If he saves $5 a week, how many weeks must he save before he can buy the toy plane?

8. Philip has 12 toy cars. He arranges them into equal groups. How many possible ways can he arrange the toy cars?

9. George has 2 crayons. Olivia has 9 times as many crayons as George. Olivia has 3 times as many crayons as Sheila.

   (a) How many crayons does Olivia have?

   (b) How many crayons does Sheila have?

   Hint: See Worked Example 2.

10. Andy has 45 marbles. Andy has 5 times as many marbles as Gerard. Harry has 4 times as many marbles as Gerard.

    (a) How many marbles does Gerard have?

    (b) How many marbles does Harry have?

6 The Four Operations of Whole Numbers

Worked Example 1

A bicycle has 2 wheels and a tricycle has 3 wheels. How many wheels do 4 bicycles and 5 tricycles have altogether?

1 bicycle has 2 wheels.

4 bicycles have 4 × 2 = 8 wheels.

1 tricycle has 3 wheels.

5 tricycles have 5 × 3 = 15 wheels.

15 + 8 = 23

4 bicycles and 5 tricycles have **23** wheels altogether.

Worked Example 2

Adrian has 8 stickers, Betty has 10 stickers, and Denise has 6 stickers. They decide to share their stickers equally among themselves. How many stickers will each of them receive?

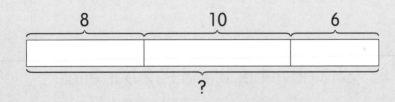

$$8 + 10 + 6 = 24$$

The three children have 24 stickers in total.

$$24 \div 3 = 8$$

Each of them will receive **8** stickers.

Worked Example 3

Lucy has 39 barrettes. After giving an equal number to each of her 4 friends, she still has 7 barrettes left. How many barrettes did she give to each friend?

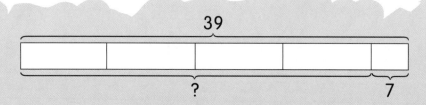

$$39 - 7 = 32$$

She gave her friends 32 barrettes.

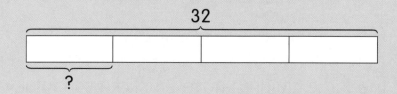

$$32 \div 4 = 8$$

She gave **8** barrettes to each friend.

Practice Questions

Answer each question carefully. Show your work and write your statement clearly.

1. Mrs. Hope wants to buy 3 T-shirts for each of her 2 granddaughters and 3 grandsons. How many T-shirts does she need?

2. Farmer Peter has 101 chickens: 60 hens and 41 roosters. There are 19 fewer ducks than chickens. How many chickens and ducks are there in all?

3. A bicycle has 2 wheels and a tricycle has 3 wheels. How many wheels do 3 bicycles and 4 tricycles have altogether?

    Hint: See Worked Example 1.

4. Rebecca has 3 times as many pens as Sarah. Sarah has 7 pens. How many pens do both have in all?

5. Isaac read a total of 78 pages of a book last weekend. This week he will read 8 pages each day from Monday to Friday. How many pages will he have read by Friday in all?

6. There are 7 rows of students in the hall. Each row has 10 students. If 17 students leave the hall, how many students remain in the hall?

7. A fruit seller had 240 apples. He sold 195 apples and packed the remaining apples in bags of 5. How many bags did he pack?

8. Andy, Ben, and Charles shared 24 stickers equally among themselves. Then Ben gave half of his stickers to Andy. How many stickers did Andy have in the end?

9. Keith has 7 shells. John has 5 more shells than Keith. Leon has 8 shells. If all three boys decide to share their shells equally, how many shells will each boy get?

10. Steven had 52 cards. After giving an equal number to each of his three neighbors, he still had 28 cards left. How many cards did he give to each neighbor?

Challenging Problems

Worked Example 1

The total length of two ropes is 55 cm. One rope is 37 cm shorter than the other. What is the length of the longer rope?

Method 1

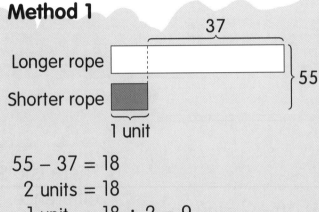

$55 - 37 = 18$
$2 \text{ units} = 18$
$1 \text{ unit} = 18 \div 2 = 9$
$37 + 9 = 46$

The length of the longer rope is **46 cm**.

Method 2

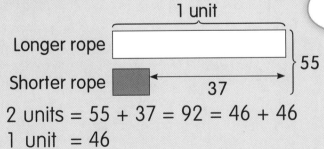

1 unit = longer rope = shorter rope + 37 cm

$2 \text{ units} = 55 + 37 = 92 = 46 + 46$
$1 \text{ unit} = 46$

The length of the longer rope is **46 cm**.

Worked Example 2

Steven has $22. Jane has $16.
(a) How much money must Steven give to Jane so that each of them will have the same amount of money?
(b) How much will each person have then?

Method 1

(a)

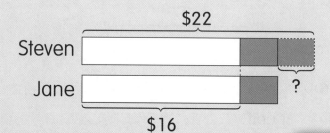

$22 − $16 = $6
$6 ÷ 2 = $3

Steven must give **$3** to Jane.

There is a $6 difference.

(b)   Steven: $22 − $3 = $19
Jane: $16 + $3 = $19

Each person will have **$19**.

Method 2

Before

$22

Steven

Jane

$16

?

$22 + $16 = $38

They both have **$38** in total.

After

Steven

Jane

38

?

$38 = $19 + $19
$22 − $19 = $3

(a) Steven must give **$3** to Jane.
(b) Each person will have **$19**.

Worked Example 3

The monorail that goes around an island is 30 m long. It has 4 cars, each 6 m long. What is the space between two neighboring cars if the cars are equally spaced apart?

$$4 \times 6 = 24$$

The total length of 4 cars is 24 m.

$$30 - 24 = 6$$

The total length of the space between the cars is 6 m.

Since there are 4 cars, there are 3 spaces altogether.

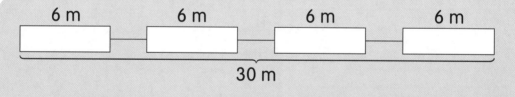

$$6 \div 3 = 2$$

The space between two neighboring cars is **2 m**.

Do these problems. Show your work and write your statements clearly.

1. The total length of two ropes is 36 in. One rope is 4 in. longer than the other. What is the length of the longer rope?

2. Nelly dreamed of two numbers. Her numbers add up to 20. When she subtracts one number from the other number, she gets 8. What are the two numbers?

3. Mindy has 32 pencils. Karen has 18 pencils.
   (a) How many pencils must Mindy give to Karen so that each of them will have the same number of pencils?
   (b) How many pencils will each person have then?

   Hint: See Worked Example 1.

4. A wooden crate can hold 280 more cartons of juice than a large plastic box. Both the crate and the box can hold 300 cartons in all. How many cartons can the plastic box hold?

5. A slow printer prints 5 pages per minute. A fast printer prints 12 pages per minute. How many more pages does the fast printer print than the slow printer in 10 minutes?

6. Lucy saves $2 a week to buy a comic book. She has saved $4. The comic book costs $16. How many more weeks must she save before she can buy the book?

7. A train has 5 cars, each 7 m long. The cars are joined by connectors of length 3 m. How long is the train?

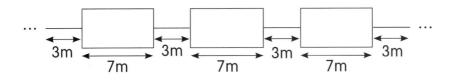

8. Damien ordered 4 books from an overseas bookstore. Each book cost the same, and there was a $5 postage charge for the order. His total bill was $33. How much did one book cost?

9. Leo used some buttons to form a square. If there are 4 buttons on each side of the square, how many buttons did he use to form the square?

10. A light-rail train takes 5 minutes to reach the next station. It stays at a station for 1 minute before heading to the next station. If Kevin boards a train at the first station on time, how long will it take him to reach the fourth station?

7 Money

Worked Example 1

Carol has $6.20. Jenny has $3.40.
(a) How much money do the two girls have in all?
(b) How much more money does Carol have than Jenny?

(a)

$6.20

| Carol |
| Jenny |

?

$3.40

$6.20 + $3.40 = $9.60

The two girls have **$9.60** in all.

(b)

$6.20

| Carol |
| Jenny |

?

$3.40

$6.20 − $3.40 = $2.80

Carol has **$2.80** more than Jenny.

Worked Example 2

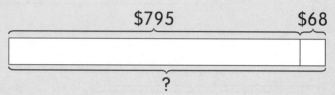

Mrs. Pine bought a TV set for $795 and a fan for $68. She paid the cashier $1,000 for the items. How much change did she receive?

Method 1

$795	$68

?

$795 + $68 = $863

The TV and the fan cost $863 altogether.

$1,000 − $863 = $137

She received **$137** change.

Method 2

$1,000 − $795 = $205

Mrs. Pine would have $205 left after paying for the TV only.

$205 − $68 = $137

She received **$137** change.

Worked Example 3

Judith and Grace had $53 altogether. After Judith spent $24 and Grace spent $17, both of them had the same amount of money left. How much did Grace have at first?

Method 1

	1 unit	$24	
Judith	▮	▯	
			} $53
Grace	▮	▯	
	?	$17	

2 units = $53 − $24 − $17 = $12
1 unit = $12 ÷ 2 = $6
1 unit + $17 = $6 + $17 = $23
Grace had **$23** at first.

Method 2

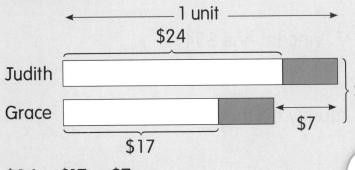

$24 − $17 = $7
2 units = $53 + $7 = $60 = $30 + $30
1 unit = $30
1 unit − $7 = $30 − $7 = $23
Grace had **$23** at first.

1 unit = amount of money Judith had = amount of money Grace had + $7

79

Practice Questions

Answer each question carefully. Show your work and write your statement clearly.

1. Pam, Kate, and Wendy each have a nickel, a dime, or a quarter. Kate's coin is worth the most. Pam's coin is worth more than Wendy's. Which coin does each girl have?

2. Peter has $35 less than Diana. If Peter has $96, how much money does Diana have?

3. Melissa has $97. Vincent has $54.
   (a) How much less money does Vincent have than Melissa?
   (b) How much money do they have in total?

4. Russell has $38. He plans to buy a printer that costs $125. How much more money does he need?

5. Anita wants to buy a box of chocolates. She has $1. After borrowing $3 from her father, she still needs $2. How much does the box of chocolates cost?

6. Mrs. Dean wants to buy 2 sacks of rice. One sack of rice costs $18. She has $28 in her purse. How much more money does she need?

7. At a department store, a pair of pants costs $78. A shirt costs $29 less than the pair of pants. How much do they cost altogether?

8. Amy bought a frying pan for $18, a table fan for $27, and a vacuum cleaner for $53. If she paid with a $100 bill, how much change did she get?

9. Sue and Becky had $38 altogether. After Sue donated $8 and Becky donated $10 to charity, both of them had the same amount of money left. How much did Becky have in the beginning?

Hint: See Worked Example 3.

10. Geraldine bought a watch for $79. The cashier gave her $21 change. How much did she give the cashier?

Challenging Problems

Worked Example 1

Joshua and his 2 brothers each receive 50¢ a day for lunch. How much will they receive in 5 days?

Joshua and his 2 brothers represent 3 persons.

$$50¢ + 50¢ + 50¢ = 150¢$$
$$= \$1.50$$

They receive $1.50 a day.

> They receive $3 in two days.

$$\underbrace{\$1.50 + \$1.50}_{\$3} + \underbrace{\$1.50 + \$1.50}_{\$3} + \$1.50 = \$6 + \$1.50$$
$$= \$7.50$$

They will receive **$7.50** in 5 days.

Worked Example 2

Theresa and Julie wish to buy a birthday card. To buy the card, Theresa needs 10¢ more, and Julie needs 40¢ more. When they combine their money, they still do not have enough money. How much does the card cost? Assume that there are only nickels, dimes, and quarters.

Card

Since Julie needs 40¢ more to buy the card, the card must cost more than 40¢.

Assume the card costs 50¢. Then Julie will have 10¢ and Theresa will have 40¢.

When they combine their money, both of them will have 40¢ + 10¢ = 50¢, which is enough to buy the card.

So, the card cannot cost **50¢**.

Let the cost of the card be 45¢. Then Julie will have 5¢ and Theresa will have 35¢.

When they combine their money, both of them will have 5¢ + 35¢ = 40¢, which is not enough to buy the card.

So, the card must cost **45¢**.

Do these problems. Show your work and write your statements clearly.

1. In a bistro, a cup of coffee costs 40¢ and a cake costs $2.50. Two students bought 2 cups of coffee and a cake. How much did they pay?

2. Joel bought a T-shirt for $7 and sold it for $8. Then he bought the same T-shirt for $9 and sold it for $10. How much money did he make in all?

3. Lucy and her 3 sisters each receive $0.75 a day for lunch. How much will they receive in 5 days?

    Hint: See Worked Example 1.

4. A ruler costs $1. An eraser costs 60¢ less than the ruler. A pen costs 2 more dimes than the eraser. How much does the pen cost?

5. Patsy and Candy have $133 altogether. Alan has $45 more than them. How much do all of them have?

6. Louis bought two watches: an expensive one and a cheap one. The cheap watch cost $8. If the expensive watch cost 4 times as much as the cheap watch, how much did he spend on both watches?

7. Gerald saves 3 quarters in the first month, 4 quarters in the second month, 5 quarters in the third month, and so on. How much money, in dollars, will he save in four months?

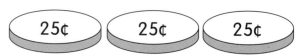

8. Jason plans to buy a pack of peanuts that costs 35¢ from a vending machine. If the machine can take nickels, dimes, and quarters in any combination, how many different combinations of coins can he use to pay for the peanuts?

9. Peter and John want to buy an eraser. Peter needs 20¢ more to buy the eraser, and John needs 10¢ more to buy the eraser. When they combine their money, they still do not have enough to buy the eraser. How much does the eraser cost? Assume that there are only nickels, dimes, and quarters.

Hint: See Worked Example 2.

10. Pauline and her 2 friends collected some empty cans and took them to the recycling center. After 4 days, they received $24 in all. If they divided the money equally among themselves, how much did each of them get?

8 Fractions

Worked Example 1

Mrs. Robinson cut a cake into 8 equal pieces. She gave 1 piece to each of her 3 neighbors and 2 pieces to her son.
(a) What fraction of the cake did she give to her neighbors?
(b) What fraction of the cake was left?

(a) Mrs. Robinson gave 3 pieces to 3 neighbors and 2 pieces to her son.

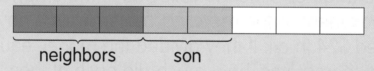

Fraction of cake given to neighbors = $\frac{3}{8}$

She gave **$\frac{3}{8}$** of the cake to her neighbors.

(b) Number of pieces remaining = 8 − 3 − 2 = 3

Fraction of cake left = $\frac{3}{8}$

$\frac{3}{8}$ of the cake was left.

Worked Example 2

Joe has some marbles. $\frac{4}{11}$ of his marbles are blue. $\frac{5}{11}$ of them are green. The rest of them are red. What fraction of his marbles are red?

Method 1

$\frac{4}{11}$ and $\frac{5}{11}$ make $\frac{9}{11}$.

9 out of 11 equal parts of marbles are blue or green.

$$11 - 9 = 2$$

2 out of 11 equal parts of marbles are red.

$\frac{2}{11}$ of his marbles are red.

Method 2

There are 11 equal parts of marbles.
4 parts are blue and 5 parts are green.

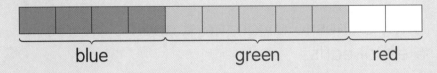

blue   green   red

2 out of 11 equal parts of marbles are red.

$\frac{2}{11}$ of his marbles are red.

Practice Questions

Answer each question carefully. Show your work and write your statement clearly.

1. Annie, Belle, Cindy, and Daisy decide to share 1 large, square pizza equally.
    (a) Show on the figure below the amount of pizza that Daisy will get.
    (b) What fraction of the pizza will Daisy get?

2. (a) Draw a line to divide the shape below into halves. How many ways can you do it?

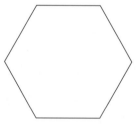

    (b) Draw 3 lines to divide the shape below into 6 equal parts.

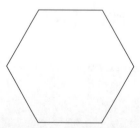

3. Mrs. Davis cut a pizza into 8 equal pieces. Her daughter and 2 sons each ate 1 piece of the pizza. What fraction of the pizza was left?

4. A chocolate bar was broken into 12 equal parts. Sharon ate 2 parts and Kent took 5 parts of the chocolate bar. What fraction of the chocolate bar was left?

5. Nathan and 4 of his friends shared a pizza equally among themselves.
   (a) How many pieces was the pizza cut into?
   (b) What fraction of the pizza did his 4 friends have in total?

6. Jacob ate $\frac{2}{6}$ of a cake and Drew ate $\frac{3}{6}$ of it. What fraction of the cake did the two boys eat?

7. Mrs. Moore baked a chicken pie for the family. She gave $\frac{7}{12}$ of the pie to her children and kept the rest in the fridge. What fraction of the pie was kept in the fridge?

8. Dale ate $\frac{3}{9}$ of a cake and Tess ate $\frac{2}{9}$ of it. What fraction of the cake was not eaten?

9. Casey borrows some library books. $\frac{3}{11}$ of the books are science books, $\frac{4}{11}$ are math books, and the rest are history books. What fraction of the library books are not history books?

10. Irene has some paper clips. $\frac{7}{12}$ of the paper clips are green. $\frac{4}{12}$ of them are yellow. The rest of them are blue. What fraction of her paper clips are blue?

Challenging Problems

Worked Example 1

There are 7 oranges to be shared equally among 4 people. How will they share the oranges?

Step 1: Give 1 orange to each person, leaving 3 oranges behind.

Step 2: Divide each of the remaining 3 oranges into quarters.

1 orange gives 4 quarters.
3 oranges give $3 \times 4 = 12$ quarters.

Step 3: Distribute the 12 quarters of oranges among the 4 people.

Each person will get another 3 quarters, or $\frac{3}{4}$ of an orange.

Each person will receive **1** whole orange and $\frac{3}{4}$ of an orange, or $1\frac{3}{4}$ oranges.

Worked Example 2

Look at the figure below.

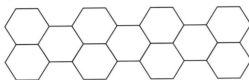

A hexagon is a six-sided figure.

(a) How many hexagons are there?
(b) Color 5 hexagons green. What fraction of the hexagons are green?
(c) Color the rest of the hexagons yellow. What fraction of hexagons are yellow?

(a) There are **11** hexagons.

(b) 5 out of 11 hexagons are green,

or $\frac{5}{11}$ of the hexagons are green.

(c) $11 - 5 = 6$

6 out of 11 hexagons are yellow,

or $\frac{6}{11}$ of the hexagons are yellow.

Worked Example 3

Mr. Danny cut a pizza into halves. His daughter, Susan, took 1 piece and divided it into 3 equal slices. She ate 1 slice and gave another slice to her friend.
(a) What fraction of the pizza did Susan eat?
(b) What fraction of the pizza was left in the end?

(a)

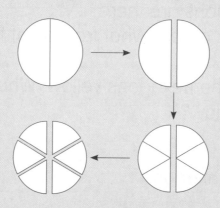

The pizza could be divided into 6 equal slices.

Number of slices of pizza that Susan ate = 1

Number of slices of pizza that her friend ate = 1

Fraction of pizza Susan ate = $\frac{1}{6}$

Susan ate $\frac{1}{6}$ of the pizza.

We may also say "$\frac{2}{3}$ of the pizza was left." Do you know why?

(b) Number of slices remaining = 6 − 1 − 1 = 4

Fraction of pizza left = $\frac{4}{6}$

$\frac{4}{6}$ of the pizza was left.

Do these problems. Show your work and write your statements clearly.

1. George gave $\frac{5}{9}$ of his stickers to his brothers and $\frac{2}{9}$ to his cousins. What fraction of his stickers did he have left?

2. Look at the clock below. What fraction of the clock lies in the shaded region between the two hands?

3. There are 5 pears for 2 students to share. How can they share the pears equally so that each of them will get the same portion?

4. There are 7 oranges for 3 children to share equally. What fraction of the oranges will each child get?

5. Pete, Phil, and Sam want to share 4 pies equally.
    (a) Color the figure below to show the amount of pies that Pete will get.
    (b) What fraction of the pies will Pete get?

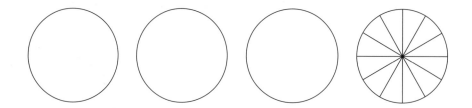

6. How can you cut a cake into 8 equal pieces with only 3 cuts?

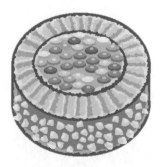

7. Look at the figure below.

(a) How many equal parts are there?
(b) Color 3 parts blue. What fraction of the figure is blue?
(c) Color 2 parts red. What fraction of figure is red?
(d) What fraction of the figure is not colored?

8. Look at the triangles below.

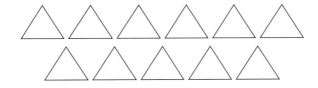

(a) How many triangles are there?
(b) Color 4 triangles green. What fraction of the triangles is green?
(c) Color the rest of the triangles yellow. What fraction of triangles is yellow?

9. Look at the container of balls.

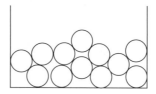

(a) How many balls are there in the container?
(b) Color half of the balls blue and half of the balls red.
If one red ball is now removed, what fraction of the
balls is blue and what fraction of the balls is red?

10. Jermaine baked a pie and cut it into halves. Amelia
took 1 piece and ate $\frac{1}{2}$ of it. What fraction of the pie did
Amelia eat?

9 Time

Worked Example 1

Hannah went to watch a movie with her friends in the morning. The time she left and returned home are shown on the clocks below. How long was Hannah away from home?

Left home

Returned home

Hannah left home at 11:30 A.M. and returned home at 4:30 P.M.

11:30 A.M. $\xrightarrow{1\text{ h}}$ 12:30 P.M. $\xrightarrow{1\text{ h}}$ 1:30 P.M.

$\downarrow$ 1 h

4:30 P.M. $\xleftarrow{1\text{ h}}$ 3:30 P.M. $\xleftarrow{1\text{ h}}$ 2:30 P.M.

1 hour + 1 hour + 1 hour + 1 hour + 1 hour = 5 hours

Hannah was away from home for **5 hours**.

Worked Example 2

Felicia left the library at 2:50 P.M.
She took 40 minutes to walk home.
What time did Felicia reach home?

40 min = 10 min + 30 min

2:50 P.M. $\xrightarrow{\text{10 min}}$ 3:00 P.M. $\xrightarrow{\text{30 min}}$ 3:30 P.M.

Felicia reached home at **3:30 P.M.**

Worked Example 3

During peak hours, 8 buses leave the terminal every 30 minutes. How many buses will leave the terminal in 1 hour? (1 hour = 60 minutes)

Let's start at 9:00 A.M.
One hour after 9:00 A.M. is 10:00 A.M.

1 hour = 60 minutes
60 min = 30 min + 30 min

There are 2 thirty minutes in one hour.

30 min	30 min
8 buses	8 buses	8 buses

9:00 P.M.	9:30 P.M.	10:00 P.M.

8 + 8 + 8 = 24

24 buses will leave the terminal in one hour.

Practice Questions

Answer each question carefully.

1. Write down the correct time for each clock.

    (a)

    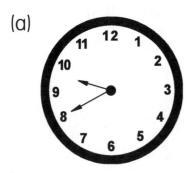

    _____

    (b)

    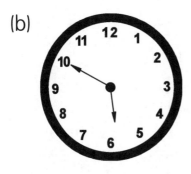

    _____

    (c)

    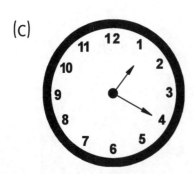

    _____

2. Mr. Walker saw the following signboard outside a bookshop.

```
OPEN DAILY
10:30 A.M. – 8:30 P.M.
```

How many hours is the shop open every day?

3. William had a violin lesson. The time he started and ended his lesson are shown on the clocks below. How long was his lesson?

Start

End

4. On a daily basis trains leave the station every half hour. The first train leaves at 9:30 A.M. What time will the sixth train leave?

5. Melinda and Betty went to see a movie in the morning. They came home half an hour before noon. What time did they reach home?

6. A children's variety program began at 11:40 A.M. It lasted 50 minutes. What time did the program end?

7. A TV show started at 9:30 A.M. and ended at 10:15 A.M.
   How long did the show last?

8. A concert began at 7:30 P.M. and lasted three hours.
   What time did the concert end?

9. Lawrence took 30 minutes to shower. He came out of the bathroom at 8:10 P.M. When did he go into the bathroom?

10. Mr. Lincoln spent an hour reading. At midnight, he had a light snack. One hour later, he went to sleep.
   (a) What time did he start reading?
   (b) What time did he go to sleep?

Challenging Problems

Worked Example 1

A movie started at 6:30 P.M. and ended at 9:00 P.M. How long did the movie last?

From 6:30 P.M. to 7:30 P.M., it is one hour.
From 7:30 P.M. to 8:30 P.M., it is one hour.
From 8:30 P.M. to 9:00 P.M., it is half an hour.

one hour + one hour + half an hour
= two and a half hours

The movie lasted **two and a half hours**.

Worked Example 2

Bryan, Monica, and Chris left school for the theater at the same time. Bryan reached the theater 1 hour before Chris. Monica reached the theater 30 minutes after Chris. Monica reached the theater at 1:30 P.M.

(a) Who reached the theater first?

(b) What time did Chris reach the theater?

(c) What time did Bryan reach the theater?

Let's draw a timeline to represent the given information.

Bryan reached the theater 1 hour before Chris.

Earlier ———————————————————————— Later
           | |
         Bryan   h   Chris

Monica reached the theater 30 minutes after Chris.

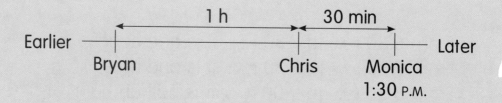

Monica reached the theater at 1:30 P.M.

(a) **Bryan** reached the theater first.

(b) Chris reached the theater 30 minutes before Monica.

$$1:30 \text{ P.M.} \xrightarrow{\text{30 min before}} 1:00 \text{ P.M.}$$

Chris reached the theater at **1:00 P.M.**

(c) Bryan reached the theater 1 hour before Chris.

$$1:00 \text{ P.M.} \xrightarrow{\text{1 h before}} 12 \text{ noon}$$

Bryan reached the theater at **12 noon**.

Worked Example 3

A shuttle bus leaves New York for Boston every two and a half hours. The first bus leaves New York at seven o'clock in the morning. What time will the fifth bus leave New York for Boston?

The first bus leaves New York at 7:00 A.M.

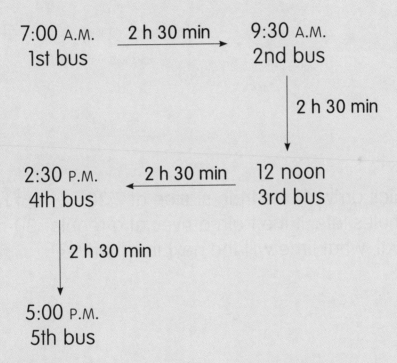

The fifth bus will leave New York at **5:00 P.M.**

Do these problems. Show your work and write your statements clearly.

1. Daphne planned to catch the 8:00 A.M. bus but she was 10 minutes late. The buses arrive regularly every half an hour.
   (a) What time did Daphne reach the bus stop?
   (b) How long did she wait for the next bus?

2. Mathias arrived at a train station at 7:20 A.M. but he was 5 minutes late. If the train arrives at a regular 30-minute interval, what time will the next train arrive?

3. When Amanda reached home from school, she rested for 30 minutes. She had her lunch for half an hour, then she spent one hour and 30 minutes doing her homework. If she finished her homework at 3:30 P.M., what time did she reach home?

4. Mathew had his dinner at 7:45 P.M. After his meal, he watched TV for 1 hour before doing some exercises for half an hour. If he stopped exercising at 9:45 P.M., how long did his dinner last?

5. Friday is 5 days before yesterday. What day is tomorrow?

6. The day before yesterday was Sunday. What is 3 days after tomorrow?

7. Stella had a piano lesson on Tuesday. Her next piano lesson will be in 2 weeks and 2 days. On what day will be her next piano lesson?

8. Darren's father is 32 years and 5 months older than Darren. His father's birthday is in February. In which month is Darren's birthday?

9. James, Kate, and Mathew left home for their swimming lesson at the same time. Mathew arrived at the swimming pool half an hour after Kate. James arrived at the swimming pool at 10:00 A.M. Mathew arrived at the swimming pool one hour before James.
   (a) Who arrived at the swimming pool first?
   (b) What time did Mathew arrive at the pool?
   (c) What time did Kate arrive at the pool?

10. During peak hours, 10 trains leave the station every 20 minutes. How many trains will leave the train in 2 hours?

10 Tables and Graphs

Worked Example 1

The graph shows the number of candies given to four children.

Pam	▲ ▲
Sue	▲ ▲ ▲ ▲ ▲
Joe	▲ ▲ ▲
Shaun	▲ ▲ ▲ ▲
Each ▲ stands for 3 candies.	

(a) How many more candies were given to Sue than Shaun?

(b) How many candies were Pam, Joe, and Shaun given in total?

(a) Sue was given $5 \times 3 = 15$ candies.
Shaun was given $4 \times 3 = 12$ candies.
$15 - 12 = 3$
Sue was given **3** more candies than Shaun.

(b) Pam was given $2 \times 3 = 6$ candies.
Joe was given $3 \times 3 = 9$ candies.
Shaun was given 12 candies.
$6 + 9 + 12 = 27$
Pam, Joe, and Shaun were given **27** candies in total.

Worked Example 2

The graph shows the mode of transport chosen by a class when they go to school every day.

Bus	◆ ◆ ◆
Car	◆
Train	◆ ◆ ◆ ◆ ◆
Walking	◆ ◆ ◆ ◆
Each ◆ stands for 4 students.	

(a) How many students take the bus to school?
(b) How many more students take the train to school than go by bus?
(c) How many more students walk to school than go by car?
(d) What is the most popular mode of transport?
(e) How many students are there in the class?

(a) 1 ◆ stands for 4 students.

   3 ◆ stand for 3 × 4 = 12 students.

   12 students take a bus to school.

(b) Train: 5 ◆ represent 5 × 4 = 20 students.

   Bus: 12 students

   20 − 12 = 8

   8 more students take the train than go by bus to school.

(c) Walking: 4 ◆ represent 4 × 4 = 16 students.

Car: 1 ◆ stands for 4 students.

16 − 4 = 12

12 more students walk to school than go by car.

or

4 ◆ − 1 ◆ = 3 ◆

3 ◆ = 3 × 4 = 12 students

12 more students walk to school than go by car.

(d) Since the graph shows that the greatest number of ◆ corresponds to the train, the most popular mode of transport is the **train**.

(e) Bus: 12 students
Car: 4 students
Train: 20 students
Walking: 16 students

12 + 4 + 20 + 16 = 52

There are **52** students in the class.

Practice Questions

Answer each question carefully.

1. The graph shows the number of shells collected by five children.

Ally	● ● ●
Bruce	● ● ● ● ●
Cally	●
Dale	● ● ● ● ●
Ellen	● ● ● ●
Each ● stands for 4 shells.	

(a) How many more shells did Bruce have than Cally?

_____

(b) How many fewer shells did Ally have than Dale?

_____

(c) How many shells did Ellen, Cally, and Ally have in total? _____

(d) Ellen plans to share her shells with Cally so that they each have the same number of shells. How many shells will each have in the end? _____

2. The graph below shows the types of sports a class of students like to do.

Badminton	★ ★ ★ ★
Softball	★ ★ ★
Basketball	★ ★
Soccer	★ ★ ★ ★ ★
Each ★ stands for 3 students.	

(a) How many students play soccer? _____

(b) How many fewer students play basketball than badminton? _____

(c) How many more students play soccer than softball? _____

(d) If 2 students switch from softball to basketball, how many students play softball now? _____

(e) How many students are there in the class altogether? _____

Challenging Problems

Worked Example 1

Mandy has more candies than Steve.
Steve has 25 candies.
Ned has fewer candies than Steve.

Use the above information to complete the graph and answer the following questions.

Each ● stands for 5 candies.

(a) Who has the most candies?
(b) How many candies does Ned have?

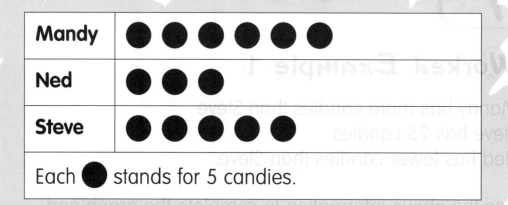

Mandy	● ● ● ● ● ●
Ned	● ● ●
Steve	● ● ● ● ●

Each ● stands for 5 candies.

Ned has fewer candies than Steve.

Less ────┼──────────┼──── More
        Ned   Steve

Mandy has more candies than Steve.

Less ────┼──────────┼──────────┼──── More
        Ned   Steve   Mandy

(a) From the number lines, **Mandy** has the most candies.

(b) If Steve has 25 candies (represented by 5 ●) and Ned has fewer candies than Steve, then 3 ● must belong to Ned. Ned has 3 × 5 = **15** candies.

Worked Example 2

A sports shop sells shoes, shirts, and bags. The graph shows the number of items sold in December.

Shoes	▲ ▲
Shirts	● ● ●
Bags	■ ■ ■ ■ ■

Each ▲ stands for 3 pairs of shoes.

Each ● stands for 5 shirts.

Each ■ stands for 4 bags.

(a) How many pairs of shoes were sold in December?

(b) The owner wanted to sell 18 shirts in December. How many more shirts did he have to sell?

(c) The shop had 25 bags at the beginning of December. How many bags did the shop have left at the end of December?

(d) In November, the shop sold twice as many pairs of shoes as in December. How many pairs of shoes did the shop sell in November?

(a) 1 ▲ stands for 3 pairs of shoes.

2 ▲ stand for 2 × 3 = 6 pairs of shoes.

6 pairs of shoes were sold in December.

(b) 1 ● stands for 5 shirts.

3 ● stand for 3 × 5 = 15 shirts.

18 − 15 = 3

The owner had to sell **3** more shirts.

(c) 1 ■ stands for 4 bags.

5 ■ stand for 5 × 4 = 20 bags.

25 − 20 = 5

The shop had **5** bags left at the end of December.

(d) In December, the shop sold 6 pairs of shoes.

2 × 6 = 12

In November, the shop sold **12** pairs of shoes.

Do these problems. Show your work and write your statements correctly.

1. Keith has fewer erasers than Steph. Steph has 6 erasers. Paul has more erasers than Steph.

   Use the above information to complete the graph and answer the following questions.

   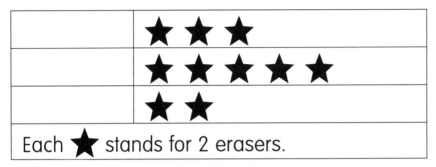

   Each ★ stands for 2 erasers.

   (a) Who has the most erasers? _____

   (b) How many erasers does Keith have? _____

2. Larry baked more cookies than Ed. Florence baked fewer cookies than Ed. Ed baked 20 cookies.

   Use the above information to complete the graph and answer the following questions.

   Each ■ stands for 5 cookies.

   (a) Who baked the most cookies? _____

   (b) How many cookies did Florence bake? _____

3. Troy collected more stickers than Tim. Tim collected more stickers than Edgar. Edgar collected 60 stickers.

Use the above information to complete the graph and answer the following questions.

Each ▲ stands for 10 stickers.

(a) Who collected the most stickers? _____
(b) How many stickers did Tim collect? _____

4. A cake shop sells muffins, tarts, and pies. The graph below shows the number of items sold on Sunday.

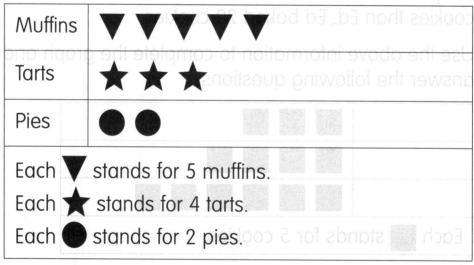

Muffins	▼ ▼ ▼ ▼ ▼
Tarts	★ ★ ★
Pies	● ●

Each ▼ stands for 5 muffins.
Each ★ stands for 4 tarts.
Each ● stands for 2 pies.

(a) How many tarts were sold on Sunday? _____
(b) The shop owner wanted to sell 20 muffins on Sunday. How many more muffins did he have to sell?

_____

(c) A pie cost $2. How much money was collected from the sale of pies? _____

(d) On Saturday, the shop sold twice as many muffins as on Sunday. How many muffins did the shop sell on Saturday? _____

5. A musical instrument shop sells recorders, guitars, and violins. The graph below shows the number of musical instruments sold in March.

Recorders	▰ ▰ ▰ ▰
Guitars	◆ ◆ ◆
Violins	▲ ▲

Each ▰ stands for 5 recorders.
Each ◆ stands for 4 guitars.
Each ▲ stands for 8 violins.

(a) How many violins were sold in March? _____

(b) The owner wanted to sell 30 recorders. How many more recorders does he need to sell? _____

(c) The shop had 25 guitars at the beginning of March. How many guitars did the shop have left at the end of March? _____

(d) A recorder costs $10. How much money was collected from the sale of recorders in March?

_____

(e) In February, the shop sold half as many guitars as in March. How many guitars did the shop sell in February? _____

11 Shapes and Patterns

Worked Example 1

Jennie plans to make an earring with 3 beads. The beads are of these shapes:

In how many ways can she arrange the beads in the earring?

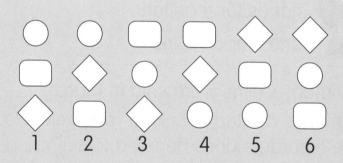

Jennie can arrange the beads in the earring in **6** different ways.

Note: List the 3 shapes in a systematic way, with one shape remaining unchanged (or "fixed") at any time, while varying the other two shapes.

Worked Example 2

If $\bigcirc + \bigcirc + \bigcirc = 9$

and $\square + \square + \bigcirc = 13$,

find the value of $\bigcirc + \bigcirc + \square$.

Method 1

Given: $\bigcirc + \bigcirc + \bigcirc = 9$

$\bigcirc = 3$

Given: $\square + \square + \bigcirc = 13$

$\square + \square + 3 = 13$

$\square + \square = 10$

$\square = 5$

$\bigcirc + \bigcirc + \square = 3 + 3 + 5$

$= \mathbf{11}$

> As soon as the value of a $\bigcirc$ is known, use this value to replace every $\bigcirc$ that appears in the other equation.

Method 2

Given: $\bigcirc + \bigcirc + \bigcirc = 9$

Given: $\square + \square + \bigcirc = 13$

$(\bigcirc + \bigcirc + \square) + (\bigcirc + \bigcirc + \square) = 9 + 13$

$= 22$

$= 11 + 11$

$(\bigcirc + \bigcirc + \square) = \mathbf{11}$

Worked Example 3

What is the missing number in each sequence?
(a) 67, 63, _____, 55, 51
(b) 1, 2, 3, 5, 8, 13, _____

(a)

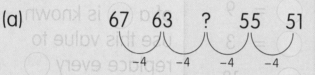

67　63　?　55　51
−4　−4　−4　−4

There is a "common difference" of 4 between 2 neighboring numbers.

$$63 - 4 = 59$$

Check : $59 - 4 = 55$

The missing number is **59**.

(b)

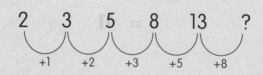

1　2　3　5　8　13　?
+1　+2　+3　+5　+8

$$13 + 8 = 21$$

The missing number is **21**.

Each number is added to the previous number to get the next.

What are the next two numbers after 21?

Practice Questions

Answer each question carefully.

1. What comes next in each of the following patterns?

   (a) ☐ ▲ △ ○ ■ △ ⬤ ☐ ☐ ▲ _____

   (b) △ △ △ △ △ △ △ △ _____

   (c) ○ △ ☐ ○ △ ☐ ○ △ _

2. Look at the pattern. What figure comes next?

3. Look at the pattern. Draw the figure that comes next.

4. What comes next in the following pattern?

5. What are the next two numbers in each of the following number patterns?

(a) 6, 11, 16, 21, 26, _____, _____

(b) 1, 3, 6, 10, 15, _____, _____

(c) 29, 22, 16, 11, 7, 4, _____, _____

6. What are the next two numbers in each of the following number patterns?

(a) 10, 9, 15, 8, 20, 7, _____, _____

(b) 2, 3, 4, 3, 4, 5, 4, 5, 6, _____, _____

7. If $\triangle$ + $\square$ = 12 and $\triangle$ + $\triangle$ + $\square$ = 21,

(a) find the value of $\triangle$, _____

(b) find the value of $\square$. _____

8. If $\square$ + $\square$ + $\square$ = $\triangledown$ + $\triangledown$,

$\square$ + $\triangledown$ = 10,

and $\bigcirc$ – $\triangledown$ = 6,

find the values of

$\square$ \qquad $\triangledown$ \qquad $\bigcirc$

_____ _____ _____

9. Look for a pattern and find the missing number.

40	10
30	20

20	10
20	50

10	60
10	20

40	10
?	40

_____

10. If $\bigcirc \times \bigcirc \times \triangle = 20$ and $\triangle + \triangle + \triangle = 15$,

find the value of $\bigcirc + \bigcirc + \triangle$.

_____

Challenging Problems

Worked Example 1

$$\diamond \times \diamond \times \diamond = 27$$

$$\square \div \diamond = \diamond$$

What number does $\square$ stand for?

Given: $\diamond \times \diamond \times \diamond = 27$

$= 3 \times 3 \times 3$

$\diamond = 3$

$\square \div \diamond = \diamond$

$\square \div 3 = 3$

$\square = 3 \times 3 = 9$

$\square$ stands for **9**.

You can also do this:

$\square = \diamond \times \diamond$

$\square = 3 \times 3 = 9$

Worked Example 2

The digits 1, 2, 3, 4, and 5 are arranged in this order:

1, 3, 4, 2, 5, 1, 3, 4, 2, 5, 1, 3, 4, 2, 5, 1, 3 …

What is the 54th number in the pattern?

1, 3, 4, 2, 5,   1, 3, 4, 2, 5,   1, 3, 4, 2, 5,

The pattern 1, 3, 4, 2, 5 repeats itself after every five digits.

How many groups of five are there?

$54 = \underline{5 \times 10} + \textcircled{4}$ ⟶ First four digits of the next group of the pattern 1, 3, 4, 2, 5

The first 50 digits are in 10 groups of the pattern 1, 3, 4, 2, 5.

51st   54th

The 54th number in the pattern is the 4th number of the 11th group, which is digit **2**.

Do these problems.

1. (a) Draw the figure that comes next.

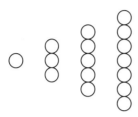

_____

(b) What is the next number?

2, 1, 4, 3, 6, 5, 8, 7, 10, 9, _____

2. If □□ = △ △ △ and

△ △ = ○ ○ ○ ○ ○ ○,

how many ○s are there in 2 □s? _____

3. If 1 ☆ = 2 ○

and 1 ○ = 3 △,

how many △s do 4 stars equal? _____

4. How many triangles are there in the figure?

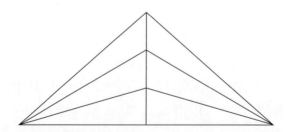

_____

5. If $\triangledown \times \triangledown \times \triangledown = 8$

   and $\bigcirc \div \triangledown = 10,$

   find the value of $\triangledown + \bigcirc$. _____

6. What is the missing number in each sequence?

   (a) 80, 40, 20, 10, _____

   (b) 3, 12, 6, 24, 9, _____, 12, 48

7. If ☆ and $\triangledown$ stand for two different numbers, what number does each shape stand for?

   ☆ + ☆ = $\triangledown$

   ☆ × ☆ = $\triangledown$

   ☆ = _____ $\triangledown$ = _____

8. The digits 1, 2, 3, and 4 are arranged in this order:

   1, 4, 3, 2, 1, 4, 3, 2, 1, 4, 3, 2, …

   What is the 99th digit in the number pattern? _____

9. (a) How many ways can you divide a rectangle into four equal parts?

   _____

(b) How many ways can you divide a square into equal parts?

[ ] _____

10. On the number chart below, the numbers 1 to 500 are placed in five columns.

A	B	C	D	E
1	2	3	4	5
6	7	8	9	10
11	12	13	14	15
16	17	18	19	20
21	22			

Which column do these numbers belong to?

(a) 50 _____   (b) 107 _____

(c) 234 _____   (d) 309 _____

(e) 433 _____

Answer each question carefully. Show your work and write your statement clearly.

1. Jackson had 83 books. He gave 15 to May. Then Jackson's godfather gave him 17 more books. How many books does Jackson have now?

2. If $\triangle + \bigcirc = 20$ and $\triangle - \bigcirc = 10$,

    (a) find the value of $\triangle$, _____

    (b) find the value of $\bigcirc$. _____

3. Robert saw 7 airplanes. Mike saw 8 airplanes. Andrew saw as many airplanes as what Robert and Mike saw altogether. How many airplanes did Andrew see?

4. A drama club has 73 members. The number of boys is 59 more than the number of girls. How many boys are there in the club?

5. Look at each pattern below. Draw the three shapes that come next.

(a)

_____ _____ _____

(b)

_____ _____ _____

6. Lulu folded 27 paper cranes. Seraphina folded 18 more paper cranes than Lulu. How many paper cranes did both Lulu and Seraphina fold together?

7. Anne took 60 minutes to read a book and Melanie took 1 hour and 30 minutes to read the same book. Who read faster?

8. How many triangles are there in the figure below?

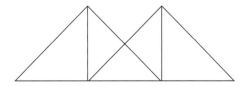

_____

9. The letters A to F are painted on blocks. A is painted on 1 block, B on 2 blocks, C on 3 blocks, and so on. How many blocks are painted altogether?

10. There were 37 people on a bus at first. At bus stop A, 12 more people boarded the bus. At bus stop B, 8 people left the bus. How many people were left on the bus?

Challenging Problems

Do these problems. Show your work and write your statements clearly.

1. Grandpa Jones is collecting his pension with his group of friends. He is both the 10th oldest and the 10th youngest senior citizen in the group. How many persons were there in the group?

2. A bicycle has 2 wheels and a tricycle has 3 wheels. 11 bicycles and tricycles have a total of 28 wheels. How many bicycles and how many tricycles are there?

3. An elevator can carry either 12 children or 8 adults. If 9 children are already in the elevator, how many adults can still get in?

4. Farmer John had some chickens and goats. The animals had a total of 13 heads and 40 feet. How many were chickens and how many were goats?

Hint: Use guess and check.

5. A spider has 8 legs and a beetle has 6 legs. 7 spiders and beetles have a total of 50 legs. How many spiders and how many beetles are there?

6. Some camels are walking in a line in the desert. 1 camel is in front of 3 camels. 1 camel is behind 3 camels. 2 camels are in the middle of the other camels. What is the least possible number of camels?

Hint: Draw a diagram.

7. Gertrude and her brother went shopping. She spent $12 on a bag and $9 on a cap. She then spent $13 on a book. If she had $8 left, how much did Gertrude have at first?

8. A 36-seater school bus picks up 1 student at the first bus stop, 2 students at the second bus stop, 3 students at the third bus stop, and so on. At which bus stop will the bus be full?

9. Mrs. Ford bought 7 children's watches from a store for gifts. The price of each watch was the same, and there was a $5 extra cost to wrap all the watches. If the total bill was $40, how much did each watch cost?

10. You have a drawer containing black and blue socks. It is midnight and the light is switched off. What is the minimum number of socks that you have to remove from the drawer to make sure you have at least one matching pair of socks?

13 Review Questions 2

Practice Questions

Answer each question carefully. Show your work and write your statements clearly.

1. Edward gave 13 pencils to Hansel and 31 pencils to James. He had 27 pencils left. How many pencils did he have at first?

2. There were 13 children at Jason's birthday party. Faith and Annie left the party at 9:00 P.M. Sarah and her twin sister left at 9:15 P.M. How many children remained at the party?

3. 4 students are lining up to buy movie tickets. Henry is between Emily and Willie. Stan is last in the line and he is standing behind Emily. Who is first in the line?

4. Christopher bought 32 postcards for Christmas. He sent 3 to his cousins, 5 to his friends, and 7 to his pen pals. How many postcards did he have left?

5. Sally saw a van, a truck, and a car crossing a bridge. The truck crossed the bridge after the car. The van crossed the bridge before the car. In which order, did the van, truck, and car cross the bridge?

Hint: Draw a number line to represent the vehicles.

6. There are 5 students in front of Mark. He is 6th from the end of the line. How many students are there in the line?

7. Fill in each blank with the correct answer.

(a) 12 less than 21 is _____.

(b) 17 less than _____ is 71.

(c) 32 is _____ more than 23.

(d) _____ is 19 more than 33.

(e) 42 is _____ less than 70.

(f) 68 is 20 more than _____.

8. If $\square$ + $\triangle$ = 30 and 23 − $\triangle$ = 5,

what is the value of $\square$? _____

9. Fill in the circles with 1, 2, 3, 4, and 5 so that the total of the numbers along each line is less than 10.

Hint: The number at the center is counted twice. Use trial and error (or guess and check).

10. Josephine saves 4 half-dollar in the first week, 5 half-dollar in the second week, 6 half-dollar in the third week, and so on. How much money will she save at the end of 4 weeks?

50¢

Challenging Problems

Do these problems. Show your work and write your statements clearly.

1. Anita saw 8 birds. Alan saw 7 birds. Rebecca saw twice as many birds as what Anita and Alan saw together. How many birds did Rebecca see?

2. Mr. Robinson took 2 minutes to cut a log into 3 pieces. How long would it take him to cut the same log into 11 pieces?

3. You take a particular two-digit number, reverse its digits to make a second two-digit number, and add these two numbers together. If the answer is 121, what are all the possible two-digit numbers?

4. There are 5 teams taking part in a contest. Each team competes only once with the other teams. How many matches are there in the contest altogether?

5. Dave is 5th in a line. Albert is 6th from the end of the line. There are 3 students lining up between Dave and Albert. How many students are there in the line?

6. Stewart has 9 toy cars. Leo has 4 times more toy cars than Stewart. How many toy cars do they have altogether?

7. Look at the set of numbers below.

1, 4, 2, 1, 4, 2, 1, 4, 2, 1, 4 ...

(a) What is the 26th number?
(b) What is the total of the first 15 numbers?

8. Isaac has $5 now. He saves $2 a day to buy a dictionary. The dictionary costs $13. How many more days must he save before he can buy the dictionary?

9. Emma made a necklace with different colored beads. She followed this pattern: 2 blue beads, then 1 red bead. The pattern was repeated. She used 6 red beads for the necklace. How many beads did she use in all?

10. Roderick read 32 pages of *Math is Fun* on Monday. He read 15 fewer pages on Monday than on Tuesday. How many pages did he read on both days?

14 Review Questions 3

Practice Questions

Answer each question carefully. Show your work and write your statements clearly.

1. Mrs. Turner made some pies. Her 5 children ate 23 pies and she gave 49 to her neighbor. There were 43 pies left. How many pies did Mrs. Turner make?

2. Karen is 8 years old. Her brother, Dan, is 6 years older than her. Their father is 23 years older than Dan. How old is their father?

3. What fraction of the figure is shaded?

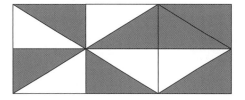

4. Using the digits 7, 2, and 9, what are the largest and smallest three-digit numbers that can be formed?

5. Fill in the missing numbers.

    (a) 25 less than _____ is 349.

    (b) 7 × 4 is _____ less than 40.

6. 7 children went on a picnic. Each child brought 2 sandwiches and 3 cookies. How many cookies did the children bring altogether?

7. A total of 66 students went to watch a movie. There were 3 buses. On 2 of the buses, there were 23 students each. How many students were there on the third bus?

8. 6 flag poles are placed at an equal distance away from each other in a row. How many spaces between the flag poles are there?

9. Fill in the boxes with the missing digits.

(a)
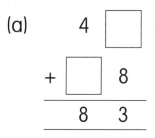

```
    4  ☐
  +  ☐  8
  ───────
    8  3
```

(b)
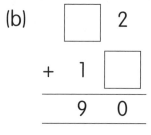

```
    ☐  2
  +  1  ☐
  ───────
    9  0
```

(c)
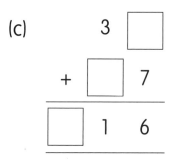

```
       3  ☐
  +  ☐  7
  ───────
  ☐  1  6
```

10. Zoe is in the middle of a line of 10 boys and 9 girls. If all
the boys line up behind the girls, in which position is Zoe
from the last child in the line?

Challenging Problems

Do these problems. Show your work and write your statements clearly.

1. Fill in the blanks.

   (a) _____ − 23 = 32

   (b) 71 is _____ more than 56.

   (c) 45 is 23 less than _____ .

   (d) 63 is _____ less than 155.

2. During peak hours, 12 buses leave a terminal every 30 minutes. How many buses will leave the terminal in one hour?

3. Tuesday is 4 days after tomorrow. Which day is 3 days before yesterday?

4. 8 trees are planted at an equal distance away from each other along a street. The distance between the second tree and the fourth tree is 10 m. How far is the eighth tree from the first one?

5. Xavier draws 10 lines in a row on a piece of paper. The lines have equal distances from one another. If two neighboring lines are 3 cm apart, how far is the tenth line from the first line?

|← 3 cm →|← 3 cm →| . . . |← 3 cm →|

6. It takes Michael 10 minutes to saw a piece of wood into 2 pieces. How long will it take him to saw the piece of wood into 5 pieces?

7. A clock strikes 4 times at 4 o'clock. It takes 6 seconds from the start of the first strike to the end of the last strike. How many seconds will it take to strike 6 times at 6 o'clock from the start to the end?

8. Some students are standing in a row, and Sally is one of them. Counting from the right to the left, Sally is in the 23rd position. Counting from the left to the right, Sally is in the 32nd position. How many students are there in the row altogether?

9. Maggie gave 6 sheets of paper to each of 4 students. There were 4 sheets of paper left. How many sheets of paper did she have at first?

10. Using each of the digits 1, 2, 3, 4, 5, 6, 7, 8, and 9 only once, fill in the circles to make three mathematical sentences.

   Hint: The product cannot exceed 9. It can be 2 × 3 = 6 or 2 × 4 = 8.

$$\bigcirc + \bigcirc = \bigcirc$$

$$\bigcirc - \bigcirc = \bigcirc$$

$$\bigcirc \times \bigcirc = \bigcirc$$

Answers

1 Addition and Subtraction

Practice Questions (pp. 3–6)

1. 180 + 70
    = 180 + 20 + 50

    =   200   + 50
    = 250
    or
    180 + 70
    = 150 + 30 + 70

    = 150 +   100
    = 250
    Mr. Brown sold **250** apples.

2. 265 + 348
    = 200 + 300 + 60 + 40 + 5 + 8

    =   500   +   100   +   13
    = 600 + 13
    = 613
    He sold **613** hotdogs on the two days.

3. 600 – 348
    = 600 – 350 + 2
    = 250 + 2
    = 252
    There are **252** cows.

4. 752 – 425
    = 752 – 422 – 3
    = 330 – 3
    = 327
    327 men attended the workshop.

5. 824 – 505
    = 824 – 500 – 5
    = 324 – 5
    = 324 – 4 – 1
    = 320 – 1
    = 319
    or
    824 – 505
    = 825 – 505 – 1
    = 320 – 1
    = 319
    319 students left the library.

6. 135 + 265
    = 100 + 200 + 30 + 60 + 5 + 5

    =   300   +   90   +   10
    = 400
    He had **400** bananas at first.

7. (a) 314 – 68
        = 314 – 14 – 50 – 4
        = 300 – 50 – 4
        = 250 – 4
        = 246
        Mike read **246** magazines.

    (b) 314 + 246
        = 310 + 240 + 4 + 6

        =   550   +   10
        = 560
        They read **560** magazines altogether.

8. (a) 409 – 238
        = 408 + 1 – 208 – 30
        = 408 – 208 – 30 + 1

        = 200 – 30 + 1
        = 170 + 1
        = 171
        June has **171** ribbons.

    (b) 409 + 171
        = 409 + 1 + 170
        = 410 + 170
        = 580
        They have **580** ribbons altogether.

9. 426 + 567
    = 426 + 564 + 3

    =   990 + 3
    = 993
    Both halls can seat **993** people altogether.

10. 857 − 168
   = 857 − 167 − 1
   = 857 − 157 − 10 − 1
   = 700 − 10 − 1
   = 690 − 1
   = 689
   Zac scored **689** points.

Challenging Problems (pp. 8–11)

1.

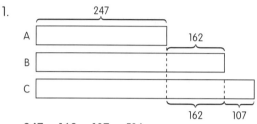

247 + 162 + 107 = 516
Team C scored **516** points.

2.

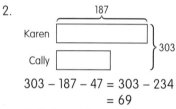

303 − 187 − 47 = 303 − 234
              = 69
Cally has **69** cards now.

3.

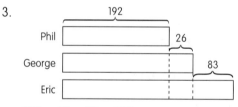

192 + 26 + 83 = 301
Eric has **301** toy cars.

4.

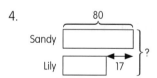

Method 1
80 − 17 = 63
Lily drew 63 drawings.
80 + 63 = 143
They drew **143** drawings in all.

Method 2
80 + 80 − 17 = 160 − 17 = 143
They drew **143** drawings in all.

5. 147 − 52 = 95
   There was an additional 95 people on
   board the train after the second station.
   308 + 127 + 95 = 530
   There were **530** passengers on board
   after the second station.

6. 120 − 25 = 120 − 20 − 5
            = 100 − 5
            = 95
   Fiona scored 95 points.
   101 + 95 = 196
   They scored **196** points in all.

7. From page 123 to page 160, there are:
   160 − 123 + 1 = 38
   76 − 38 = 38
   She read 38 pages from page 202
   onwards.
   202 + 38 − 1 = 239
   She stopped reading at page **239**.

8. *Method 1*
   520 − 230 = 290
   290 − 74 = 216
   Annie has **216** beads left.

   Method 2
   Instead of finding the number of beads
   Annie has, we may solve the question as
   follows:
   230 + 74 = 304
   520 − 304 = 216
   Annie has **216** beads left.

9. 19 + 17
   = 19 + 1 + 16
   = 20 + 16
   = 36
   There are 36 red and green buttons.

   51 − 36
   = 51 − 31 − 5
   = 20 − 5
   = 15
   There are 15 blue buttons.

   19 − 15 = 4
   He has **4** more red than blue buttons.

10. *Method 1*

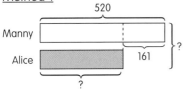

520 − 161 = 359
Alicia has **359** ribbons.
520 + 359 = 879
They have **879** ribbons altogether.

Method 2
520 + 520 = 1040
1040 − 161 = 879
They have **879** ribbons altogether.

2 Length

Practice Questions (pp. 14–17)

1. 174 − 37 = 174 − 34 − 3
     = 140 − 3
     = 137
    Benjamin's sister is **137 cm** tall.

2.

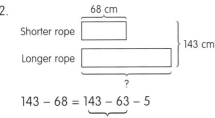

143 − 68 = 143 − 63 − 5
 =   80 − 5
 = 75
The length of the longer rope is **75 cm**.

3. 105 + 67 = 105 + 65 + 2
     =   170 + 2
     = 172
    Stick N is **172 cm** long.

4.

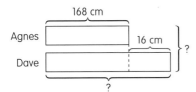

(a) 168 + 16 = 184
     Dave is **184 cm** tall.
(b) 168 + 184 = 352
     The total height of Agnes and Dave is **352 cm**.

5. 182 − 37 = 182 − 32 − 5
     = 150 − 5
     = 145
    The red ant covered **145 cm**.

6.

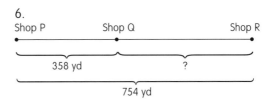

754 − 358 = 754 − 354 − 4
 = 400 − 4
 = 396
The distance between shops Q and R is **396 yd**.

7. *Method 1*
    405 + 398 = 405 + 400 − 2
     = 805 − 2
     = 803
    Flynn walked **803 m** altogether.

    Method 2
    405 + 398 = 400 + 2 + 398 + 3
     = 400 + 400 + 3
     = 803
    Flynn walked **803 m** altogether.

8. 200 − 131 = 200 − 130 − 1
     = 70 − 1
     = 69
    The shorter girl is **69 cm** tall.

9. 128 + 347 = 125 + 347 + 3
     = 125 + 350
     = 475
    The ribbon was **475 cm** long at first.

10. 950 − 805 = 950 − 800 − 5
     = 150 − 5
     = 145
    Tom's school is **145 m** farther from his house than from his aunt's house.

Challenging Problems (pp. 21–24)

1. 218 + 168 + 294 = 218 + 162 + 6 + 294
     =   380   +   300
     = 680
    Suzie will have jogged **680 m**.

2.

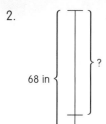

68 − 9 = 68 − 8 − 1
     = 60 − 1
     = 59
Bradley is 59 in. tall.

59 − 9 = 50
Bradley is **50 in.** taller than the stool.

3. 318 + 205 + 135 = 318 + 340
                  = 658
Patty jogged **658 m** in all.

4.

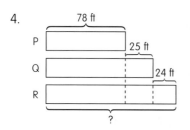

78 + 25 + 24 = 78 + 22 + 3 + 24
           = 100 + 27
           = 127
Rope R is **127 ft** long.

5.

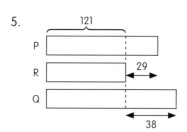

Method 1
38 − 29 = 9
121 + 9 = 130
String Q is **130 in.** long.

Method 2
121 − 29 = 92
92 + 38 = 130
String Q is **130 in.** long.

In Method 1, one can find the length of string Q without finding the length of string R.

6. Length of longer ribbon
    = 78 + 23 = 101 cm
Total length = 101 cm + 78 cm
            = 179 cm
The total length of both ribbons is **179 cm**.

7.

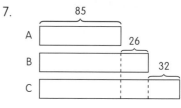

85 + 26 + 32 = 143
Rope C is **143 cm** long.

8.

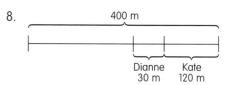

(a) 400 − 120 = 280
     Kate is **280 m** from the starting point.

(b) 280 − 30 = 250
     Dianne is **250 m** from the starting line.

9.

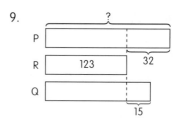

138 − 15 = 123
The length of string R is 123 cm.
123 + 32 = 155
The length of string P is **155 cm**.

10. *Method 1*

Day	Height from bottom of the well
1	4 − 2 = 2
2	2 + 4 = 6

It will take the ant **2** days to climb out of the well.

Method 2

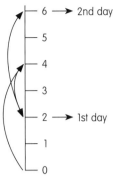

It will take the ant **2** days to climb out of the well.

3 Multiplication and Division by 2 and 3

Practice Questions (pp. 28–31)

1. $24 \div 3 = 8$
    He will have **8** groups of marbles.

2.

    $18 = 2 \times 9$ or $18 \div 2 = 9$
    Lily has **9** dolls.

3. 1 watch has 3 hands.
    4 watches have $4 \times 3 = 12$ hands.
    The watches have **12** hands in all.

4. 1 deer has 2 ears.
    9 deer have $9 \times 2 = 18$ ears.
    9 deer have **18** ears.

5.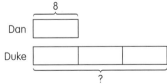

    $3 \times 8 = 24$
    Duke has **24** cakes.

6. Mr. and Mrs. Duncan and their child represent 3 persons.
    $27 \div 3 = 9$ or $27 = 3 \times 9$
    The price of one ticket was **$9**.

7. Girls: $20 \div 2 = 10$
    Boys: $10 \div 1 = 10$
    Each group is made up of 2 girls and 1 boy.
    Mr. Davies can form a total of **10** groups.

8. 1 album has 10 photos.
    3 albums have $3 \times 10 = 30$ photos.
    3 such albums will have **30** photos.

9. 12 pears = 3 pears × 4 groups
    3 pears cost $1.
    12 pears cost $4 \times \$1 = \$4$.
    She paid **$4**.

    Note: There is no need to find the price of one pear.

10. 1 bicycle has 2 wheels.
    $20 \div 2 = 10$ or $20 = 10 \times 2$
    There are **10** bicycles in his shop.

Challenging Problems (pp. 34–37)

1. 15 big buttons = 3 big buttons x 5
    For every 3 big buttons, she used 2 small buttons.
    For every 15 big buttons, she used $5 \times 2 = 10$ small buttons.
    Mrs. Amy used **10** small buttons.

2.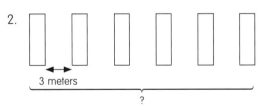

    3 meters

    Among the 6 trees, there are 5 intervals, or 5 spaces.
    Each interval measures 3 m.
    5 intervals measure $5 \times 3 = 15$ m.
    The last tree is **15 m** away from the first tree.

3.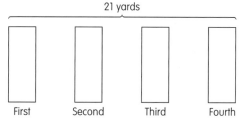

24 ÷ 3 = 8 or 24 = 8 × 3
There are **8** rows.

4. Mother rabbit + 2 baby rabbits represent 3 rabbits.
In 1 day, they eat 3 carrots.
In 4 days, they eat 4 × 3 = 12 carrots.
This rabbit family will eat **12** carrots in 4 days.

5. 1st time ⟶ 2 balls
2nd time ⟶ 4 balls
3rd time ⟶ 6 balls
4th time ⟶ 8 balls
5th time ⟶ 10 balls

He will juggle **10** balls when he goes on stage the fifth time.

6.

21 yards

| First | Second | Third | Fourth |

3 intervals measure 21 yards.
1 interval measures 21 ÷ 3 = 7 yards.
The distance between two trees next to each other is **7 yd**.

7.

Number of boys	Number of girls	Total number of tarts
2	5	2 × 3 + 5 × 2 = 6 + 10 = 16 ✗
3	4	3 × 3 + 4 × 2 = 9 + 8 = 17 ✗
4	3	4 × 3 + 3 × 2 = 12 + 6 = 18 ✔

There were **3** girls at the party.

8. Groups of 2: 2, 4, **6**, 8, 10, …
Groups of 3: 3, **6**, 9, …
Agnes has **6** balloons.

9.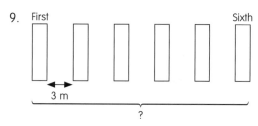

3 m

From the 1st to the 6th lamp post, there are 5 intervals.
Each interval measures 3 meters.
5 intervals measure 5 × 3 = 15 meters.
The sixth lamp post is **15 m** away from the first lamp post.

10.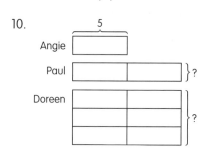

Method 1
6 × 5 = 30
Doreen has **30** stamps.

Method 2
2 × 5 = 10
Peter has 10 stamps.

3 × 10 = 30
Doreen has **30** stamps.

4 Mental Calculation

Practice Questions (pp. 41–44)

1. (a) 88   (b) 93   (c) 296   (d) 202

2. (a) 13   (b) 28   (c) 306   (d) 24

3. 28 + 72 = 100
100 − 38 = 62
The number is **62**.

4. 9 + 10 + 7 + 3 = 9 + 10 + 10
　　　　　　　= 29
The total number of potted plants sold is **29**.

5. $22 + 44 + 56$
    $= 22 + 100$
    $= 122$
    The total number of stamps in the three albums is **122**.

6. $47 + 126 + 43$
    $= 47 + 43 + 126$
    $= 90 + 126$
    $= 90 + 10 + 116$
    $= 100 + 116$
    $= 216$
    The total number of bottles of mineral water sold in three days is **216**.

7. $82 + 97 + 73$
    $= 82 + 170$
    $= 2 + 80 + 170$
    $= 2 + \quad 250$
    $= 252$
    or
    $82 + 97 + 73$
    $= 82 + 97 + 3 + 70$
    $= 82 + \quad 100 \quad + 70$
    $= \quad 182 \quad + 70$
    $= 252$
    The total number of coupons collected is **252**.

8. $97 - 49 = 100 - 50 - 3 + 1$
    $\qquad\qquad = 50 - 2$
    $\qquad\qquad = 48$
    or
    $97 - 49 = 97 - 47 - 2$
    $\qquad\qquad = 50 - 2$
    $\qquad\qquad = 48$
    He made **48** tuna sandwiches.

9. $\$256 - \$98 = \$256 - \$100 + \$2$
    $\qquad\qquad\quad = \$156 + \$2$
    $\qquad\qquad\quad = \$158$
    Edward has **$158**.

10. $102 - 97 = 102 - 100 + 3$
    $\qquad\qquad\ = 2 + 3$
    $\qquad\qquad\ = 5$
    or
    $102 - 97 = 100 - 97 + 2$
    $\qquad\qquad\ = 3 + 2$
    $\qquad\qquad\ = 5$
    There are **5** apples.

Challenging Problems (pp. 47–49)

1. (a) 93   (b) 98

2. (a) 49   (b) 39

3. (a) 167   (b) 471

4. (a) 126   (b) 724

5. $163 + 97 - 49$
    $= 160 + 3 + 97 - 49$
    $= 160 + \quad 100 \quad - 49$
    $= \quad\quad 260 \quad\quad - 49$
    $= 260 - 50 + 1$
    $= \quad\quad 210 \quad + 1$
    $= \mathbf{211}$

6. $39 + 8 + 28 + 22$
    $= 39 + 1 + 7 + 50$
    $= 40 + 50 + 7$
    $= \quad\quad 90 + 7$
    $= 97$
    The total number of buttons in the 4 boxes is **97**.

7. $105 + 89$
    $= 104 + 1 + 89$
    $= 104 + \ 90$
    $= 194$
    194 eggs were laid in all.

8. $59 + 38 + 63$
    $= 60 + 40 + 63 - 1 - 2$
    $= \quad 100 \ + \quad 60$
    $= 160$
    The total number of hamsters sold is **160**.

9. $131 - 43$
    $= 131 - 41 - 2$
    $= 131 - 31 - 10 - 2$
    $= \quad 100 \quad - 10 - 2$
    $= \quad\quad 90 - 2$
    $= 88$
    or
    $131 - 43 = 100 - 40 + 31 - 3$
    $\qquad\qquad\ = 60 + 28$
    $\qquad\qquad\ = 88$
    88 stickers are in the second box.

10. $115 - 78 = 115 - 80 + 2$
    $ = 35 + 2$
    $ = 37$
    or
    $115 - 78 = 118 - 78 - 3$
    $ = 40 - 3$
    $ = 37$
    37 cookies were left.

5 Multiplication and Division by 4, 5, and 10

Practice Questions (pp. 52–55)

1. (a) 1 student needs 4 notebooks.
       5 students need 5×4
       $= 20$ notebooks.
       5 students need **20** notebooks.

   (b) 8 students need 8×4
       $= 32$ notebooks.
       8 students need **32** notebooks.

2. 1 shirt has 5 buttons.
   7 shirts have $7 \times 5 = 35$ buttons.
   There are **35** buttons altogether.

3. 2 girls and 6 boys represent 8 children.
   $80 \div 8 = 10$
   Each child received **10** books.

4. 1 plant has 6 roses.
   10 plants have $10 \times 6 = 60$ roses.
   There are **60** roses altogether.

5. $30 = 6 \times 5$
   There are 6 groups of 5 oranges.
   5 oranges cost $3.
   30 oranges cost $6 \times \$3 = \$18$
   He paid **$18**.

6. Each box has $3 + 2 = 5$ pens.
   $10 \times 5 = 50$
   She has **50** pens altogether.

7. Each necklace has $3 + 5$
   $= 8$ beads.
   $4 \times 8 = 32$
   She has **32** beads in total.

8. $40 \div 8 = 5$
   5 vans will be needed to transport all the people.

9. $36 \div 9 = 4$
   4 tables are needed to seat 36 students.

10. There are 4 persons.
    $24 \div 4 = 6$
    Each person will get **6** bookmarks.

Challenging Problems (pp. 58–61)

1.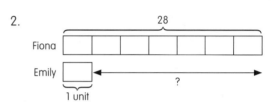

   $5 \times 10 = 50$
   They have **50** markers in all.

2.

   Fiona

   Emily

   1 unit

   From the model,
   7 units = 28
   1 unit = $28 \div 7 = 4$
   6 units = $6 \times 4 = 24$
   Fiona has **24** more ribbons than Emily.

3. First floor
      ↕ 10 steps
   Second floor

   Third floor

   Fourth floor

   Fifth floor

   Sixth floor

   $5 \times 10 = 50$
   She has to climb **50** steps from the first floor to reach her home.

4. Judith and her 7 friends represent 8 persons.
   $2 + 3 = 5$
   $8 \times 5 = 40$
   There were **40** lollipops and strawberries altogether.

5. 2   3   4   5
    $2 \times 3 = 6$ $3 \times 4 = 12$ $4 \times 5 = 20$
    $2 \times 4 = 8$ $3 \times 5 = 15$
    $2 \times 5 = 10$
    6 different answers can be formed.
    Note: $3 \times 2 = 2 \times 3$; $4 \times 2 = 2 \times 4$; $4 \times 3 = 3 \times 4$;
    $5 \times 4 = 4 \times 5$

6. (a) $24 = \underbrace{4 \times 6}$ or $24 \div 6 = 4$

          4 groups of 6
          4 groups can be formed.

    (b) $24 = \underbrace{3 \times 8}$ or $24 \div 8 = 3$

          3 groups of 8
          3 groups can be formed.

7. $45 \div 5 = 9$
    He must save for **9** weeks.

8. $12 = 1 \times 12$ 1 group of 12
    $ = 2 \times 6$ 2 groups of 6
    $ = 3 \times 4$ 3 groups of 4
    $ = 4 \times 3$ 4 groups of 3
    $ = 6 \times 2$ 6 groups of 2
    $ = 12 \times 1$ 12 groups of 1
    Philip can arrange the toy cars in
    6 possible ways.

9.
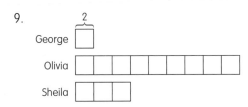

    (a) $9 \times 2 = 18$
         Olivia has **18** crayons.

    (b) $18 \div 3 = 6$
         Sheila has **6** crayons.

10.
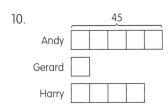

    (a) $45 \div 5 = 9$
         Gerard has **9** marbles.

    (b) $4 \times 9 = 36$
         Harry has **36** marbles.

6 The Four Operations of Whole Numbers

Practice Questions (pp. 65–68)

1. 2 granddaughters + 3 grandsons
    = 5 persons
    1 person receives 3 T-shirts.
    5 persons receive $5 \times 3 = 15$ T-shirts.
    She needs **15** T-shirts.

2.
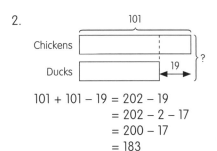

    $101 + 101 - 19 = 202 - 19$
    $ = 202 - 2 - 17$
    $ = 200 - 17$
    $ = 183$
    There are **183** chickens and ducks in all.

3. 1 bicycle has 2 wheels.
    3 bicycles have $3 \times 2 = 6$ wheels.
    1 tricycle has 3 wheels.
    4 tricycles have $4 \times 3 = 12$ wheels.
    $6 + 12 = 18$
    3 bicycles and 4 tricycles have **18** wheels
    altogether.

4.
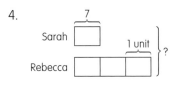

    1 unit = 7
    4 units = $4 \times 7 = 28$
    Both have **28** pens in all.

5. From Monday to Friday, there are 5 days.
    In 1 day, he reads 8 pages.
    In 5 days, he reads $5 \times 8 = 40$ pages.
    $78 + 40 = 118$
    He will have read **118** pages in all.

6. 1 row has 10 students.
    7 rows have $7 \times 10 = 70$ students.
    $70 - 17 = 70 - 20 + 3$
    $ = 50 + 3$
    $ = 53$
    53 students remain in the hall.

7. 240 − 195 = 240 − 200 + 5
                    = 40 + 5
                    = 45
    He had 45 apples left.
    45 ÷ 5 = 9
    He packed **9** bags.

8. 24 ÷ 3 = 8
    Each boy had 8 stickers.
    8 ÷ 2 = 4
    Ben gave 4 stickers to Andy.
    8 + 4 = 12
    Andy had **12** stickers in the end.

9. 7 + 5 = 12
    John has 12 shells.
    7 + 12 + 8 = 27
    The 3 boys share 27 shells equally
    among themselves.
    27 ÷ 3 = 9
    Each boy will get **9** shells.

10. 52 − 28 = 52 − 30 + 2
                    = 22 + 2
                    = 24
    Steven gave away 24 cards.
    24 ÷ 3 = 8
    He gave **8** cards to each neighbor.

Challenging Problems (pp. 73–76)

1.
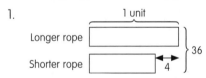

    2 units = 36 + 4 = 40 = 20 + 20
    1 unit = 20
    The length of the longer rope is **20 in**.

2.
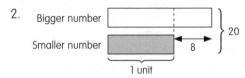

    2 units = 20 − 8 = 12 = 6 + 6
    1 unit = 6
    1 unit + 8 = 6 + 8 = 14
    The two numbers are **6** and **14**.

3.
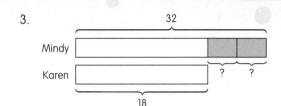

    (a) 32 − 18 = 14
         14 ÷ 2 = 7
         Mindy must give Karen **7** pencils.

    (b) Mindy: 32 − 7 = 25
         Karen: 18 + 7 = 25
         Each person will have **25** pencils then.

4.

    2 units = 300 − 280 = 20
    1 unit = 10
    The plastic box can hold **10** cartons.

5. *Method 1*
    12 − 5 = 7
    In 1 minute, the fast printer prints 7 more
    pages.
    In 10 minutes, the fast printer prints 10 × 7
    = **70** more pages.

    Method 2
    In 1 minute, the slow printer prints 5 pages.
    In 10 minutes, the slow printer prints
    10 × 5 = 50 pages.

    In 1 minute, the fast printer prints 12 pages.
    In 10 minutes, the slow printer prints
    12 × 10 = 120 pages.

    120 − 50 = 70
    The fast printer prints **70** more pages.

6. $16 − $4 = $12
    She has $12 more to save.
    12 ÷ 2 = 6
    She must save for **6** more weeks before
    she can buy the book.

7.
    Each interval is 3 m long.
    4 intervals are 4 × 3 = 12 m long.

There are 5 cars.
Each car is 7 m long.
5 cars are 5 × 7 = 35 m long
35 + 12 = 47
The train is **47 m** long.

8. $33 − $5 = $28
The 4 books cost a total of $28.
$28 = 4 × $7
One book cost **$7**.

9.
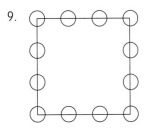
4 corners have 4 buttons.
4 sides have 4 × 2 = 8 buttons.
4 + 8 = 12
He used **12** buttons to form the square.

10.
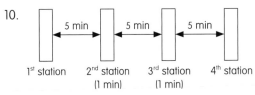
1st station   2nd station   3rd station   4th station
                  (1 min)   (1 min)

3 traveling intervals take 3 × 5
= 15 minutes.
2 waiting times take 2 × 1 = 2 minutes.
15 + 2 = 17
It will take him **17 minutes** to reach the fourth station.

7 Money

Practice Questions (pp. 80–83)

1. Nickel: 5¢ → **Wendy**
Dime: 10¢ → **Pam**
Quarter: 25¢ → **Kate**

2.
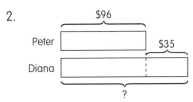
$96 + $35 = $96 + $4 + $31
            = $100 + $31
            = $131
Diana has **$131**.

3.
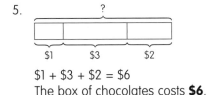
(a) $97 − $54 = $94 − $54 + $3
              = $40 + $3
              = $43
Vincent has **$43** less than Melissa.

(b) $97 + $54 = $97 + $3 + $51
              = $100 + $51
              = $151
They have **$151** in total.

4. $125 − $38 = $87
He needs **$87** more.

5.
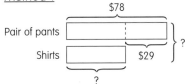
$1 + $3 + $2 = $6
The box of chocolates costs **$6**.

6. $18 + $18 = $36
2 sacks of rice cost $36.
$36 − $28 = $36 − $26 − $2
              = $10 − $2
              = $8
She needs **$8** more.

7. *Method 1*
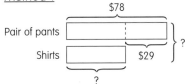
$78 − $29 = $78 − $28 − $1
             = $50 − $1
             = $49
The shirt costs $49.
$78 + $49 = $78 + $50 − $1
             = $128 − $1
             = $127
They cost **$127** altogether.

Method 2
$78 + $78 = $80 + $80 − $2
             = $160 − $4
             = $156

$156 - $29 = $156 - $30 + $1
            = $126 + $1
            = $127
They cost **$127** altogether.

8. $18 + $27 + $53 = $18 + $80
                   = $98
    $80
    The three items cost $98.
    $100 - $98 = $2
    Amy got **$2** change.

9.
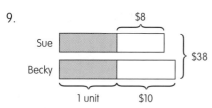

    2 units = $38 - $8 - $10
            = $30 - $10
            = $20
            = $10 + $10
    1 unit = $10
    1 unit + $10
    $10 + $10 = $20
    Becky had **$20** in the beginning.

10.
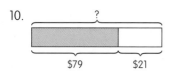

    $79 + $21 = $100
    She gave the cashier **$100**.

Challenging Problems (pp. 86–89)

1. 2 × 40¢ + $2.50 = 80¢ + 250¢
                    = 330¢
                    = $3.30
    They paid **$3.30**.

2. $8 - $7 = $1
    Joel first made $1.

    $10 - $9 = $1
    He next made $1.

    $1 + $1 = $2
    He made **$2** in all.

3. $0.75 = 75¢
    4 × 75 = 300
    Lucy and her 3 sisters receive $3 a day.

5 × $3 = $15
They will receive **$15** in 5 days.

4. $1 = 100 ¢
    100¢ - 60¢ = 40¢
    An eraser costs 40¢.

    40¢ + 20¢ = 60¢
    The pen costs **60¢**.

5.
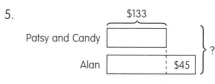

    $133 + $133 + $45 = $311
    All of them have **$311**.

6.
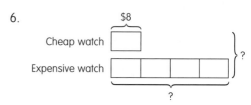

    5 × $8 = $40
    He spent **$40** on both watches.

7. 3 + 4 + 5 + 6 = 18
    18 × 25¢ = 9 × 2 × 25¢
             = 9 × 50¢
             = 450¢
             = $4.50
    He will save **$4.50** in four months.

8. 35 = 5 × 7 (seven 5¢ coins)
       = 5 × 5 + 10 (five 5¢ + one 10¢)
       = 5 × 3 + 20
         (three 5¢ + one 20¢)
       = 5 × 3 + 2 × 10
         (three 5¢ + two 10¢)
       = 5 × 1 + 20 + 10
         (one 5¢ + one 20¢ + one 10¢)
       = 5 × 1 + 3 × 10 (one 5¢ + three 10¢)
    He can use **6** different combinations of
    coins to pay for the peanuts.

9. If the eraser costs 30¢, then Peter has
    10¢ and John has 20¢. In total, Peter
    and John will have 30¢, which is enough
    to pay for the eraser. So, the eraser cannot
    cost 30¢.

If the eraser costs 25¢, then Peter has 5¢ and John has 15¢. In total, they have 5¢ + 15¢ = 20¢, which is 5¢ short of the 25¢ eraser. So, the eraser must cost **25¢**.

10. Pauline and her two friends represent 3 persons.
$24 = 3 × $8
Each of them got **$8**.

8 Fractions

Practice Questions (pp. 92–95)

1. Four possible cuttings are shown below.

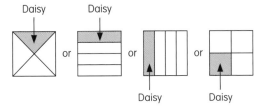

Daisy   Daisy   or   or   or

Daisy   Daisy

Accept all possible answers.

(b) Daisy will get $\frac{1}{4}$ of the pizza.

2. (a)

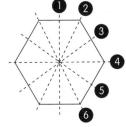

There are many ways to divide the shape into 2 parts. The dotted lines above show 6 out of the many possible ways. Accept all possible answers.

(b)

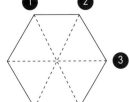

3. The daughter and two sons ate 3 out of the 8 equal pieces.
$8 - 3 = 5$
$\frac{5}{8}$ of the pizza was left.

4. $2 + 5 = 7$
Sharon and Kent both took 7 equal parts.
$12 - 7 = 5$
$\frac{5}{12}$ of the chocolate bar was left.

5. (a) Nathan and his friends represent 5 persons.
The pizza was cut into **5** pieces.

(b) 1 person → $\frac{1}{5}$ of the pizza

4 persons → $\frac{1}{5} + \frac{1}{5} + \frac{1}{5} + \frac{1}{5} = \frac{4}{5}$

His 4 friends had $\frac{4}{5}$ of the pizza in total.

6. Jacob ate 2 out of 6 equal parts of the cake.
Drew ate 3 out of 6 equal parts of the cake.
$2 + 3 = 5$
The two boys ate $\frac{5}{6}$ of the cake.

7. Mrs. Moore gave 7 out of 12 equal parts to her children.
$12 - 7 = 5$

$\frac{5}{12}$ of the pie was kept in the fridge.

8. Dale ate 3 and Tess ate 2 out of 9 equal parts of the cake.
$9 - 2 - 3 = 4$
$\frac{4}{9}$ of the cake was not eaten.

9.

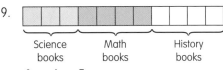

Science books   Math books   History books

$\frac{3}{11} + \frac{4}{11} = \frac{7}{11}$

$\frac{7}{11}$ of the library books are not history books.

10. $\frac{7}{12} + \frac{4}{12} = \frac{11}{12}$

11 parts out of 12 equal parts are green and yellow paper clips.

$12 - 11 = 1$

$\frac{1}{12}$ of her paper clips are blue.

Challenging Problems (pp. 99–102)

1. George gave 5 out of 9 equal parts to his brothers, and 2 out of 9 equal parts to his cousins.

   $9 - 5 - 2 = 2$

   He had 2 out of 9 equal parts left.

   He had $\frac{2}{9}$ of his stickers left.

2. There are 12 intervals round the clock. 5 intervals from the number 7 to the number 12 are shaded.

   $\frac{5}{12}$ of the clock lies in the shaded region.

3. Step 1: Give 2 pears to each student, leaving 1 pear behind.

   Step 2: Divide the remaining pear into halves. 1 pear gives 2 halves.

   Step 3: Distribute the 2 halves equally. Each student will receive 1 half.
   Each student will receive **2** whole pears and $\frac{1}{2}$ of a pear.

4. Step 1: Give 2 oranges to each child, leaving 1 orange behind.

   Step 2: Divide the remaining orange into 3 parts.

   Step 3: Give 1 third of the orange to each child.
   Each child will receive **2** whole oranges and $\frac{1}{3}$ of an orange, or $2\frac{1}{3}$ oranges.

5. (a) & (b)

Pete   Phil   Sam

   Step 1: Give 1 pie to each child, leaving 1 extra pie to be shared among 3 children.

   Step 2: Divide the remaining pie into 3 parts, with each child receiving $\frac{1}{3}$ of a pie.
   Each child will get 1 pie and $\frac{1}{3}$ of a pie.

   Pete will receive **1 whole** and $\frac{1}{3}$ of all the pies.

6. Make 2 cuts from the top to get 4 equal pieces. Make 1 cut across from the side of the cake to get 8 equal pieces.

7. (a) There are **10** equal parts.

   (b) 3 out of 10 parts of the figure should be shaded blue.
   $\frac{3}{10}$ of the figure is blue.

   (c) 2 out of 10 parts of the figure should be shaded red.
   $\frac{2}{10}$ of the figure is red.

   (d) 5 out of 10 equal parts are not colored.
   $\frac{5}{10}$ of the figure is not colored.

8. (a) There are **11** triangles.

   (b) 4 out of 11 triangles should be colored green.
   $\frac{4}{11}$ of the triangles are green.

   (c) $11 - 4 = 7$
   7 out of 11 triangles should be colored yellow.
   $\frac{7}{12}$ of the triangles are yellow.

9. (a) There are **12** balls in the container.

   (b) After coloring, there are 6 blue balls and 6 red balls.
   If 1 red ball is removed, there are 5 red balls and 6 blue balls left.
   Fraction of the balls that are blue = $\frac{6}{11}$

   Fraction of the balls that are red = $\frac{5}{11}$

   Note: There is no change in the number of blue balls.

10.

   From the diagram, $\frac{1}{4}$ of the pie is eaten. Amelia ate $\frac{1}{4}$ of the pie.

9 Time

Practice Questions (pp. 106–110)

1. (a) **9:40**   (b) **5:50**   (c) **1:20**

2.
$$+\tfrac{1}{2}\text{h} \qquad +1\,\text{h} \qquad +8\,\text{h} \qquad +\tfrac{1}{2}\text{h}$$
10:30 A.M. → 11:00 A.M. → 12 noon → 8:00 P.M. → 8:30 P.M.

$$1 + \frac{1}{2} + 8 + \frac{1}{2} = 9 + 1 = 10$$

The shop is open for **10 hours** every day.

3. He started his lesson at 3:40 P.M.
   He ended his lesson at 4:20 P.M.
   $$+20\,\text{min} \qquad +20\,\text{min}$$
   3:40 P.M. → 4:00 P.M. → 4:20 P.M.

   20 min + 20 min = 40 min
   His lesson was **40 minutes** long.

4.
$$+\tfrac{1}{2}\text{h} \quad +\tfrac{1}{2}\text{h} \quad +\tfrac{1}{2}\text{h} \quad +\tfrac{1}{2}\text{h} \quad +\tfrac{1}{2}\text{h}$$

| 1st | 2nd | 3rd | 4th | 5th | 6th |

9:30 A.M.   ?

$$\frac{1}{2} + \frac{1}{2} + \frac{1}{2} + \frac{1}{2} + \frac{1}{2}$$
$$= \underbrace{1} + \underbrace{1} + \frac{1}{2}$$
$$= 2 + \frac{1}{2}$$

$$+\tfrac{1}{2}\text{h} \qquad +2\,\text{h}$$
9:30 A.M. → 10:00 A.M. → 12 noon

The sixth train will leave at **12 noon**.

5.
$$-\tfrac{1}{2}\text{ hour}$$
12 noon → 11:30 A.M.
or
Half past eleven in the morning.
They reached home at **11:30 A.M.**

6. 50 min = 20 min + 30 min
   $$+20\,\text{min} \qquad +30\,\text{min}$$
   11:40 A.M. → 12:00 noon → 12:30 P.M.

   The program ended at **12:30 P.M.**

7.
$$+30\,\text{min} \qquad +15\,\text{min}$$
9:30 A.M. → 10:00 A.M. → 10:15 A.M.

30 min + 15 min = 45 min
The show lasted **45 minutes**.

8.
$$+3\,\text{h}$$
7:30 P.M. → 10:30 P.M.
The concert ended at **10:30 P.M.**

9. 30 min = 10 min + 20 min
   $$-10\,\text{min} \qquad -20\,\text{min}$$
   8:10 P.M. → 8:00 P.M. → 7:40 P.M.
   He went into the bathroom at **7:40 P.M.**

10.
$$-1\,\text{hour}$$
Midnight → 11:00 P.M.
$$+1\,\text{hour}$$
Midnight → 1:00 A.M.

(a) He started reading at **11:00 P.M.**
(b) He went to sleep at **1:00 A.M.**

Challenging Problems (pp. 114–117)

1. (a) 8:00 A.M. + 10 min = 8:10 A.M.
   Daphne reached the bus stop
   10 minutes after 8:00 A.M., which is
   at **8:10 A.M.**

   (b) The bus after 8:00 A.M. arrives at
   8:30 A.M.
   $$+20\,\text{min}$$
   8:10 A.M. → 8:30 A.M.

   She waited **20 minutes** for the
   next bus.

2. 7:20 A.M. − 5 min = 7:15 A.M.
   The train arrived at 7:15 A.M.
   7:15 A.M. + 30 min = 7:45 A.M.
   The next train will arrive at **7:45 A.M.**

3. *Method 1*
   $$+1\,\text{h}$$
   ? $\xrightarrow{+30\,\text{min}}$? $\xrightarrow{+30\,\text{min}}$? $\xrightarrow{30\,\text{min}}$ 3:30 P.M.

   $$-1\,\text{h}$$
   1:00 P.M. $\xleftarrow{-30\,\text{min}}$ 1:30 P.M. $\xleftarrow{-30\,\text{min}}$ 2:00 P.M. $\xleftarrow{30\,\text{min}}$ 3:30 P.M.

   She reached home at **1:00 P.M.**

   Method 2

   $$30\text{ min} + \frac{1}{2}\text{h} + 1\text{ h } 30\text{ min}$$
   $$= \underbrace{30\text{ min} + 30\text{ min}} + 1\text{ h } 30\text{ min}$$
   $$= \qquad\qquad 1\text{ h} + 1\text{ h } 30\text{ min}$$
   $$= 2\text{ h } 30\text{ min}$$

   $$-30\,\text{min} \qquad -2\,\text{h}$$
   3:30 P.M. → 3:00 P.M. → 1:00 P.M.

   She reached home at **1:00 P.M.**

4.

+ 2 h
7:45 P.M. ⟶ 9:45 P.M.

Meal + TV + Exercise = 2 h

1 h   30 min
1 h 30 min

2 h – 1 h – 30 min = 1 h – 30 min
= 30 min

The dinner lasted for **30 minutes**.

5.

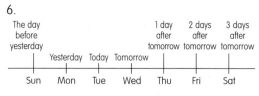

                          Yesterday   Today   Tomorrow

Fri   Sat   Sun   Mon   Tue   Wed   Thu   Fri

Tomorrow is **Friday**.

6.

The day before yesterday				1 day after tomorrow	2 days after tomorrow	3 days after tomorrow

                Yesterday   Today   Tomorrow

Sun   Mon   Tue   Wed   Thu   Fri   Sat

3 days after tomorrow is **Saturday**.

7.

         1 week   2 weeks   2 weeks
Now   later   later   + 2 days

Tue   Tue   Tue   Thu

Her next piano lesson will be on **Thursday**.

8. Darren's father is 32 years and 5 months older than him.
Every year, the father's birthday is always in February.
32 years later, the father's birthday still falls in February.
Now, 5 months after February is July.
So, Darren's birthday is in **July**.

9.

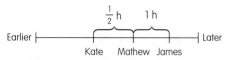

             $\frac{1}{2}$ h   1 h

Earlier ⊢   ⊣ Later

         Kate   Mathew   James

(a) **Kate** arrived first.

(b)

– 1 hour
10:00 A.M. ⟶ 9:00 A.M.

Mathew arrived at the pool at **9:00 A.M.**

(c)

$-\frac{1}{2}$ hour
9:00 A.M. ⟶ 8:30 A.M.

Kate arrived at the pool at **8:30 A.M.**

10. 1 hour = 60 minutes
2 hours = 120 minutes = 6 × 20 minutes
There are six 20 minutes in 2 hours.
Let's start at 8:00 A.M.

10 trains	10 trains	10 trains	10 trains	10 trains	10 trains	10 trains
	20 min	20 min	20 min	20 min	20 min	20 min

8:00 A.M.   10:00 A.M.

7 × 10 = 70
70 trains will leave the train station in 2 hours.

10 Tables and Graphs

Practice Questions (pp. 121–122)

1. (a) 1 ● stands for 4 shells.
5 ● stand for 5 × 4 = 20 shells.
The number of shells Bruce has is 20.
The number of shells Cally has is 1 × 4 = 4.
20 – 4 = 16
Bruce had **16** more shells than Cally.

(b) 3 ● stand for 3 × 4 = 12 shells.
Number of shells Ally has = 12.
5 ● stand for 5 × 4 = 20 shells.
Number of shells Dale has is 20.
20 – 12 = 8
Ally had **8** fewer shells than Dale.

(c) 4 ● stand for 4 × 4 = 16 shells.
Number of shells Ellen is 16
Number of shells Cally is 4
Number of shells Ally is 12
16 + 12 + 4 = 32
Ellen, Cally, and Ally had **32** shells in total.

(d) 16 + 4 = 20
20 ÷ 2 = 10
Each will have **10** shells.

2. (a) 1 ★ stands for 3 students.

5 ★ stand for 5 × 3 = 15 students.

15 students play soccer.

(b) 2 ★ stand for 2 × 3 = 6 students.

Number of students who play basketball = 6

4 ★ stand for 4 × 3 = 12 students.

Number of students who play badminton = 12

12 – 6 = 6

6 fewer students play basketball than badminton.

(c) Number of students who play soccer = 15

3 ★ stand for 3 × 3 = 9 students.

Number of students who play softball = 9

15 – 9 = 6

6 more students play soccer than softball.

(d) Number of students who play softball = 9

9 – 2 = 7

7 students play softball now.

e) Number of students who play badminton = 12
Number of students who play softball = 9
Number of students who play basketball = 6
Number of students who play football = 15

12 + 9 + 6 + 15 = 42

There are **42** students in the class altogether.

Challenging Problems (pp. 127–129)

1.

Steph	★ ★ ★
Paul	★ ★ ★ ★ ★
Keith	★ ★
Each ★ stands for 2 erasers.	

Keith has fewer erasers than Steph.

Kevin has more erasers than Steph.

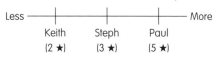

(a) From the number line, **Paul** has the most erasers.

(b) Keith has 2 × 2 = **4** erasers.

2.

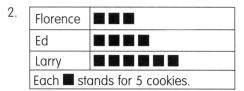

Each ■ stands for 5 cookies.

Florence baked fewer cookies than Ed.

Larry baked more cookies than Ed.

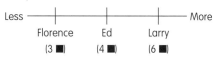

(a) From the number line, **Larry** baked the most cookies.

(b) Florence   Ed
   3 ■   4 ■
      20 cookies

4 ■ stand for 20 cookies.

1 ■ stands for 20 ÷ 4 = 5 cookies.

3 ■ stand for 3 × 5 = 15 cookies.

Florence baked **15** cookies.

3.

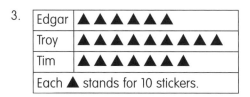

Each ▲ stands for 10 stickers.

Tim collected more stickers than Edgar.

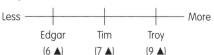

Troy collected more stickers than Tim.

(a) From the number line, **Troy** collected the most stickers.

(b) Edger: 6 ▲
Tim: 7 ▲

6 ▲ stand for 60 stickers.

1 ▲ stands for 60 ÷ 6 = 10 stickers.

7 ▲ stand for 7 × 10 = 70 stickers.

Tim collected **70** stickers.

4. (a) 1 ★ stands for 4 tarts.
3 ★ stand for 3 × 4 = 12 tarts.
12 tarts were sold on Sunday.

(b) 1 ▼ stands for 5 muffins.
5 ▼ stand for 5 × 5 = 25 muffins.
25 – 20 = 5
He had to sell **5** more muffins.

(c) 1 ● stands for 2 pies.
2 ● stand for 2 × 2 = 4 pies.
4 × $2 = $8
$8 was collected from the sale of pies.

(d) Number of muffins sold on Sunday = 25
25 + 25 = 50
50 muffins were sold on Saturday.

5. (a) 1 ▲ stands for 8 violins.
2 ▲ stand for 2 × 8 = 16 violins.
16 violins were sold in March.

(b) 1 ■ stands for 5 recorders.
4 ■ stand for 4 × 5 = 20 recorders.
30 – 20 = 10
He needs to sell **10** more recorders.

(c) 1 ◆ stands for 4 guitars.
3 ◆ stand for 3 × 4 = 12 guitars.
25 – 12 = 13
The shop had **13** guitars left at the end of March.

(d) Number of recorders sold = 20
20 × $10 = $200
$200 was collected from the sale of the recorders in March.

(e) Number of guitars sold in March = 12
12 ÷ 2 = 6
The shop sold **6** guitars in February.

11 Shapes and Patterns

Practice Questions (pp. 133–135)

1. (a)   (b)

(c)

2. 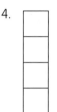   3.

4.

5. (a)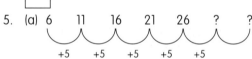

5 is added to the number to get the next number.

The next two numbers are **31, 36**.

(b)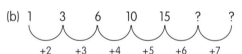

Add 2 to the first number. Then each time, add a number that is 1 larger than the previous number added.

The next two numbers are **21, 28**.

(c)

Subtract 7 from the first number. Then each time subtract a number that is one smaller than the previous number subtracted.

The next two numbers are **2, 1**.

6. (a)

There are 2 patterns observed.

First pattern: Add 5 to the first number to get the third number. Continue to add 5 to get the number required, as shown in the diagram.

Second pattern: Subtract 1 from the second number to get the fourth number. Continue to subtract 1 to get the number required, as shown in diagram.

The next two numbers are **25**, **6**.

(b) 2, 3, 4,   3, 4, 5,   4, 5, 6

The numbers are grouped in threes. Each of the three numbers of the next group increases by 1.

The next two numbers are **5**, **6**.

7. (a)
$$\triangle + \square = 12$$
$$\triangle + \triangle + \square = 21$$
$$\triangle + \quad 12 \quad = 21$$
$$\triangle = 21 - 12$$
$$= \mathbf{9}$$

(b)
$$\triangle + \square = 12$$
$$9 + \square = 12$$
$$\square = 12 - 9$$
$$= \mathbf{3}$$

8. $\square + \square + \square = \triangledown + \triangledown$ (given)

$\square + \square + \square + \square + \square$

$= \triangledown + \triangledown + \square + \square$

$= \square + \triangledown + \square + \triangledown$

     10   10

$= 10 + 10$
$= 20$
$= 4 + 4 + 4 + 4 + 4$
$\square = \mathbf{4}$ $\triangledown = \mathbf{6}$ $\bigcirc = \mathbf{12}$

9. $40 + 10 + 20 + 30 = 100$

$20 + 10 + 50 + 20 = 100$
$10 + 60 + 20 + 10 = 100$
$40 + 10 + 40 + ? = 100$
$90 + ? = 100$
$? = 100 - 90$
$? = \mathbf{10}$

10. $\triangle + \triangle + \triangle = 15$ (given)
$= 5 + 5 + 5$
$\triangle = 5$

$\bigcirc \times \bigcirc \times \triangle = 20$ (given)
$\bigcirc \times \bigcirc \times 5 = 20$
$\bigcirc \times \bigcirc = 20 \div 5$
$= 4$
$= 2 \times 2$
$\bigcirc = 2$
$\bigcirc + \bigcirc + \triangle = 2 + 2 + 5$
$= \mathbf{9}$

Challenging Problems (pp. 138–140)

1. (a)

From the first pattern, 1 circle is added on each side to get the next pattern. In the fifth pattern, 4 circles have been added on each side of the first pattern.

(b)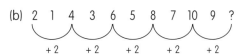

There are 2 patterns here. Since we only need to find the next term, we will use the pattern that will help us find the answer. From the first number, add 2 to get the third number. Continue to add 2 to get the term required, as shown in the diagram.

The next number is **12**.

or

2 1 4 3 6 5 8 7 10 9 ?

−1 +3 −1 +3 −1 +3 −1 +3 −1 +3

There are 2 patterns. First, we subtract

1 to get the next number, then add 3 to get the number after that. Continue to subtract 1 then add 3 to get the term required.

The next number is **12**.

2. $\triangle \triangle = \bigcirc\bigcirc\bigcirc\bigcirc\bigcirc$ (given)

   $\triangle = \bigcirc\bigcirc\bigcirc$

   $\square\square = \triangle\triangle\triangle$ (given)

   $\square\square = \bigcirc\bigcirc\bigcirc\bigcirc\bigcirc\bigcirc\bigcirc\bigcirc\bigcirc$

   $2\square = 9\bigcirc$

   There are **9** $\bigcirc$s in 2 $\square$s.

3. $1\bigcirc = 3\triangle$ (given)

   $2\bigcirc = 6\triangle$

   $2\stackrel{\star}{} = 1\bigcirc$ (given)

   $\qquad = 2 \times 3\triangle$

   $\qquad = 6\triangle$

   $1\stackrel{\star}{} = 6\triangle$

   $4\stackrel{\star}{} = 4 \times 6\triangle$

   $\qquad = 24\triangle$

   4 stars equal to **24** $\triangle$s.

4.

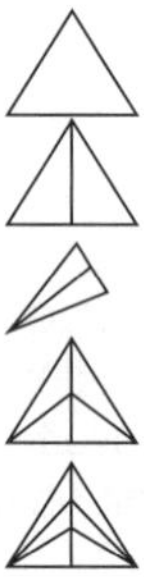

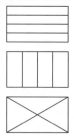

   $1 + 2 + 4 + 2 + 6 = 15$

   There are **15** triangles in the figure.

5. $\nabla \times \nabla \times \nabla = 8$ (given)

   $\qquad\qquad = 2 \times 2 \times 2$

   $\qquad \nabla = 2$

   $\bigcirc \div \nabla = 10$

   $\bigcirc \div 2 = 10$

   $\qquad \bigcirc = 10 \times 2 = 20$

   Now, $\nabla + \bigcirc = 2 + 20$

   $\qquad\qquad = \mathbf{22}$

6. (a)

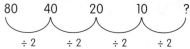

   $80 \quad 40 \quad 20 \quad 10 \quad ?$

   $\div 2 \quad \div 2 \quad \div 2 \quad \div 2$

   Divide the number by 2 to get the next number.

   The missing number is **5**.

   (b) $3 \quad 12 \quad 6 \quad 24 \quad 9 \quad ? \quad 12 \quad 48$

   $+ 12 \quad\quad + 12 \quad\quad + 12$

   There are 2 patterns observed. We will use the pattern that will help us to find the missing number.

   Add 12 until the number required is obtained as shown in the diagram.

   The missing number is **36**.

7. $\stackrel{\star}{} + \stackrel{\star}{} = \stackrel{\star}{} \times \stackrel{\star}{}$

   $2 + 2 = 2 \times 2$

   $\qquad = 4$

   $\stackrel{\star}{} = \mathbf{2}, \nabla = \mathbf{4}$

8. The pattern 1, 4, 3, 2 repeats itself.

   $99 = \underbrace{4 \times 24}_{\substack{24 \text{ groups} \\ \text{of 4 digit}}} + \underbrace{3}_{\substack{\text{3rd digit in 1, 4, 3, 2} \\ \text{is 3}}}$

   The 99th digit in the number pattern is **3**.

9. (a) Many ways exist, 3 of which are shown below:

   (b) There are an infinite or endless number of ways to divide a square into equal parts.

10. Column A: numbers that end in 1 or 6.
    Column B: numbers that end in 2 or 7.
    Column C: numbers that end in 3 or 8.
    Column D: numbers that end in 4 or 9.
    Column E: numbers that end in 5 or 0.
    (a) **E** (b) **B** (c) **D** (d) **D** (e) **C**

Review Questions 1

Practice Questions (pp. 141–144)

1. $83 - 15 = 83 - 13 - 2$
    $= 70 - 2$
    $= 68$
    $68 + 17 = 68 + 12 + 5$
    $= 80 + 5$
    $= 85$

    Jackson has **85** books now.

2. *Method 1*

    (a) $\triangle + \bigcirc + \triangle - \bigcirc = 20 + 10$
    $\triangle + \triangle + \bigcirc - \bigcirc = 30$
    $\triangle + \triangle = 30 = 15 + 15$
    $\triangle = \mathbf{15}$

    (b) $15 + \bigcirc = 20$
    $\bigcirc = \mathbf{5}$

    Method 2

    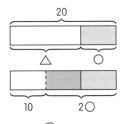

    (a) $2\bigcirc = 20 - 10 = 10$
    $\bigcirc = \mathbf{5}$

    (b) $\triangle + 5 = 20$
    $\triangle = 20 - 5 = \mathbf{15}$

3. $7 + 8 = 7 + 3 + 5$
    $= 10 + 5$
    $= 15$

    or

    $7 + 8 = 5 + 2 + 8$
    $= 5 + 10$
    $= 15$

    Andrew saw **15** airplanes.

4.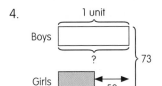

    $2 \text{ units} \rightarrow 73 + 59$
    $= 132$
    $= 66 + 66$
    $1 \text{ unit} \rightarrow 66$

    There are **66** boys in the club.

5. (a) $\square \ \triangle \ \bigcirc$

    (b) $\triangle \ \square \ \square$

6.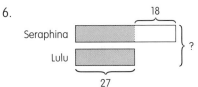

    $27 + 27 + 18$
    $= 27 + 3 + 27 + 3 + 12$
    $= \quad 30 \quad + \quad 30 \quad + 12$
    $= 72$

    Lulu and Seraphina folded **72** paper cranes.

7. 1 hour and 30 minutes
    $= 60 \text{ minutes} + 30 \text{ minutes}$
    $= 90 \text{ minutes}$

    Anne read faster.

8.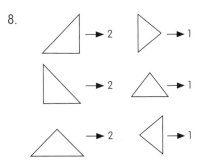

    Total number of triangles
    $= 2 + 2 + 2 + 1 + 1 + 1$
    $= 9$

    There are **9** triangles in the figure.

9.

Letter	Number of blocks
A	1
B	2
C	3
D	4
E	5
F	6

$1 + 2 + 3 + 4 + 5 + 6 = 21$

21 blocks are painted altogether.

10. $12 - 8 = 4$

There was an extra of 4 people after bus stop B.

$37 + 4 = 41$

41 people were left on the bus.

Challenging Problems (pp. 145–148)

1.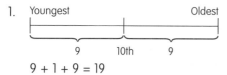

$9 + 1 + 9 = 19$

There were **19** persons in the group.

2.

Bicycles	Tricycles	Total number of wheels	Check
3	8	$3 \times 2 + 8 \times 3 = 6 + 24 = 30$	✗
4	7	$4 \times 2 + 7 \times 3 = 8 + 21 = 29$	✗
5	6	$5 \times 2 + 6 \times 3 = 10 + 18 = 28$	✓

There are **5** bicycles and **6** tricycles.

3. 12 children weigh as heavy as 8 adults.
6 children weigh as heavy as 4 adults.
3 children weigh as heavy as 2 adults.
9 children weigh as heavy as
$4 + 2 = 6$ adults.
$8 - 6 = 2$

2 adults can still get in the elevator.

4. _Method 1_

Chickens	Goats	Total number of feet	Check
8	5	36	✗
7	6	38	✗
6	7	40	✓

There were **6** chickens and **7** goats.

Method 2

Suppose there were 13 chickens. Then, there would be a total of $13 \times 2 = 26$ feet.

But there were 40 feet, so the extra $40 - 26 = 14$ feet must have come from the goats.

A goat has 2 more feet than a chicken. So, there were $14 \div 2 = 7$ goats and $13 - 7 = 6$ chickens.

There were **6** chickens and **7** goats.

5.

Spiders	Beetles	Total number of legs	Check
6	1	$6 \times 8 + 1 \times 6 = 48 + 6 = 54$	✗
5	2	$5 \times 8 + 2 \times 6 = 40 + 12 = 52$	✗
4	3	$4 \times 8 + 3 \times 6 = 32 + 18 = 50$	✓

There are **4** spiders and **3** beetles.

6.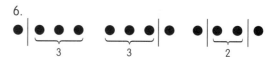

The least possible number of camels is **4**.

7. $12 + 9 + 13 + 8$
$= 12 + 8 + 9 + 11 + 2$
$= \quad 20 \quad + \quad 20 \quad + 2$
$= 42$

Gertrude had **$42** at first.

8.

Bus stop	Number of students
1	1
2	$1 + 2 = 3$
3	$3 + 3 = 6$
4	$6 + 4 = 10$
5	$10 + 5 = 15$
6	$15 + 6 = 21$
7	$21 + 7 = 28$
8	$28 + 8 = \boxed{36}$

The bus will be full at the **8th** bus stop.

9. $40 - 5 = 35$
7 watches cost $35.
$35 = 7 \times 5$
Each watch cost **$5**.

10. The first two socks taken from the drawer could be: black, blue, or blue, black. The third sock could be black or blue, and it will match any of the first two already taken out from the drawer.

   Note: The best case occurs when we have the first two socks of the same color: blue, blue; or black, black.

Review Questions 2

Practice Questions (pp. 149–152)

1. $13 + 31 + 27$
   $= 13 + 27 + 31$
   $= 40 + 31$
   $= 71$
   He had **71** pencils at first.

2. Faith and Annie represent 2 children. Sarah and her twin sister represent another 2 children.
   $13 - 2 - 2 = 9$
   9 children remained at the party.

3. Stan   Emily   Henry   Willie
   •————————————————————————————————•
   End

   Willie is first in the line.

4. $3 + 5 + 7 = 15$
   Christopher sent 15 postcards altogether.

   $32 - 15 = 32 - 12 - 3$
   $\qquad\quad = 20 - 3$
   $\qquad\quad = 17$

   He had **17** postcards left.

5. truck   car   van
   •————————————————————————————————•
   End

   The vehicles crossed the bridge in this order: **van, car, truck**.

6. 5 students   5 students
   ⏞————————•————————⏞
            Mark

   $5 + 1 + 5 = 11$
   There are **11** students in the line.

7. (a)
   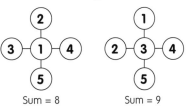
   $? = 21 - 12$
   $\quad = 9$

(b)
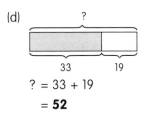
$? = 71 + 17$
$\quad = 88$

(c)
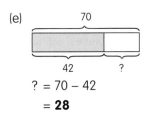
$? = 32 - 23$
$\quad = 9$

(d)
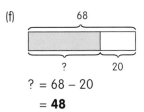
$? = 33 + 19$
$\quad = 52$

(e)
$? = 70 - 42$
$\quad = 28$

(f)
$? = 68 - 20$
$\quad = 48$

8. $23 - \triangle = 5$ (given)
   $\qquad \triangle = 23 - 5 = 18$
   $\square + \triangle = 30$ (given)
   $\square + 18 = 30$
   $\qquad \square = 30 - 18 = $ **12**

9. If 1 and 3 are in the middle circle, we have the following.

   Sum = 8   Sum = 9

   Moreover, both sums are not 10.

10.

Week	Amount saved
1	4 × 50¢ = 200¢ = $2.00
2	5 × 50¢ = 250¢ = $2.50
3	6 × 50¢ = 300¢ = $3.00
4	7 × 50¢ = 350¢ = $3.50
Total	$2 + $2.50 + $3 + $3.50 = $2 + $3 + $2.50 + $3.50 = $5 + $6 = $11

She will save **$11** at the end of 4 weeks.

Challenging Problems (pp. 153–156)

1. 8 + 7 = 15
    Anita and Alan saw 15 birds.
    2 × 15 = 30
    Rebecca saw **30** birds.

2.
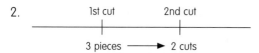

    3 pieces ⟶ 2 cuts

    To cut the log into 11 pieces, Mr. Robinson
    would need 10 cuts.

    2 cuts take 2 minutes.

    1 cut takes 1 minute.

    10 cuts take 10 minutes.

    It would take him **10** minutes to cut the
    log into 11 pieces.

3. We look for pairs of numbers of the form
    ab such that ab + ba = 121.
    We look for two whole numbers a and b
    that add up to 11.
    The possible two-digit numbers could be:
    29, 38, 47, 56, 65, 74, 83, and **92**.

4.
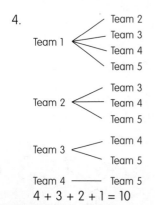

    4 + 3 + 2 + 1 = 10

    There are **10** matches in the contest
    altogether.

5.
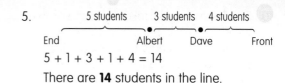

    5 + 1 + 3 + 1 + 4 = 14

    There are **14** students in the line.

6.
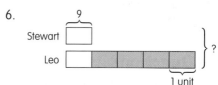

    1 unit = 9
    6 units = 6 × 9 = 54
    They have **54** toy cars altogether.

7. 1, 4, 2, 1, 4, 2, 1, 4, 2, ...

    The pattern "1, 4, 2" repeats itself.

    (a) 26 = 3 × 8 + ②

    8 groups of 3   2nd digit in
                        "1, 4, 2" is 4.

    The 26th number is **4**.

    (b) 15 = 5 × 3 (5 groups of 3)
         1 + 4 + 2 = 7
         Each group has a sum of 7.
         5 × 7 = 35
         The total of the first 15 numbers is **35**.

8. 13 − 5 = 8
    Isaac needs another $8 to buy the
    dictionary.
    8 = 4 × 2
    He needs **4** more days to save before he
    can buy the dictionary.

9.

    Blue Blue Red   Blue Blue Red

    For every red bead she used, she
    needed 2 blue beads.

    For 6 red beads, she would need
    6 × 2 = 12 blue beads.

    6 + 12 = 18

    She used **18** beads in all.

10. _Method 1_

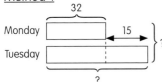

$32 + 15 = 47$

He read 47 pages on Tuesday.

$32 + 47 = 79$

He read **79** pages on both days.

Method 2

$32 + 32 + 15 = 79$

He read **79** pages on both days.

Review Questions 3

Practice Questions (pp. 157–160)

1. $23 + 49 + 43 = 20 + 40 + 40 + 3 + 9 + 3$
    $$= 100 + 15 = 115$$

    Mrs. Turner made **115** pies.

2. $8 + 6 = 14$
    Dan is 14 years old.
    $14 + 23 = 37$
    Their father is **37** years old.

3. Out of 12 equal parts, 7 parts are shaded.
    $\frac{7}{12}$ of the figure is shaded.

4. The largest 3-digit number is **972**.
    The smallest 3-digit number is **279**.

5. (a)

    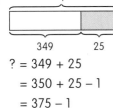

    $? = 349 + 25$
    $$= 350 + 25 - 1$$
    $$= 375 - 1$$
    $$= \mathbf{374}$$

    (b) $7 \times 4 = 28$
    28 is _____ less than 40.

    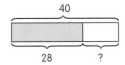

    $? = 40 - 28 = \mathbf{12}$

6. $7 \times 3 = 21$
    The children brought **21** cookies altogether.

    Note: The sandwiches are not counted.

7. $2 \times 23 = 23 + 23 = 46$
    There were 46 students on the first 2 buses.
    $66 - 46 = 20$
    There were **20** students on the third bus.

8.

    1st   6th

    $6 - 1 = 5$

    There are **5** spaces between the flag poles.

9. (a)

    ```
          4   a
      +   b   8
      ─────────
          8   3
    ```

    $a + 8 = 13$
    $a = 13 - 8$
    $a = \mathbf{5}$

    $1 \text{ (carry)} + 4 + b = 8$
    $5 + b = 8$
    $b = \mathbf{3}$

    (b)

    ```
          b   2
      +   1   a
      ─────────
          9   0
    ```

    $2 + a = 10$
    $a = 10 - 2$
    $= \mathbf{8}$

    $1 \text{ (carry)} + b + 1 = 9$
    $b + 2 = 9$
    $b = 9 - 2$
    $= \mathbf{7}$

    (c)

    ```
          3   a
      +   b   7
      ─────────
      c   1   6
    ```

    $a + 7 = 16$
    $a = 16 - 7$
    $= \mathbf{9}$

$$1 \text{ (carry)} + 3 + b = 11$$
$$4 + b = 11$$
$$b = 11 - 4$$
$$= \mathbf{7}$$
$$1 + 0 = c$$
$$c = \mathbf{1}$$

10.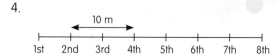

From the last child in the line, Zoe is the **11th**.

Challenging Problems (pp. 161–164)

1. (a)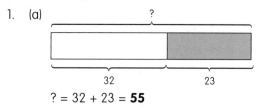

$? = 32 + 23 = \mathbf{55}$

(b)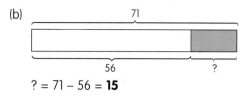

$? = 71 - 56 = \mathbf{15}$

(c)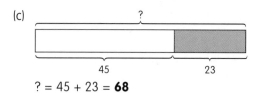

$? = 45 + 23 = \mathbf{68}$

(d)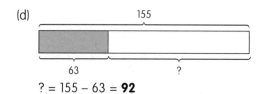

$? = 155 - 63 = \mathbf{92}$

2.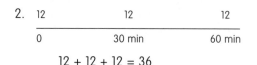

$12 + 12 + 12 = 36$

36 buses will leave the terminal in one hour.

3.

The day is **Sunday**.

4.

From the 2nd to the 4th tree, there are 2 intervals.

From the 1st to the 8th tree, there are 7 intervals.

2 intervals are 10 m long.

1 interval is 5 m long.

7 intervals are $7 \times 5 = 35$ m long.

The distance from the first tree to the eighth tree is **35 m**.

5.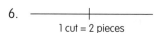

10 lines = 9 intervals

1 interval is 3 cm long.

9 intervals will be $9 \times 3 = 27$ cm long

The distance from the first line to the tenth line is **27 cm**.

6.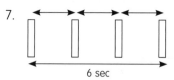

To saw the piece of wood into 5 pieces, Michael needs to saw it 4 times.

1 sawing takes 10 minutes.

4 sawings take $4 \times 10 = 40$ minutes.

It will take him **40** minutes to saw the piece of wood into 5 pieces.

7.

4 times = 3 intervals

6 times = 5 intervals

3 intervals take 6 seconds.

1 interval takes 2 seconds.

5 intervals take $5 \times 2 = 10$ seconds.

It will take **10 seconds** for the clock to strike 6 times.

8.

$$31 + 1 + 22 = 54$$

There are **54** students in the row altogether.

9. $6 \times 4 = 24$

Maggie gave 24 sheets to 4 students.

$$24 + 4 = 28$$

She had **28** sheets of paper at first.

10. In $\bigcirc \times \bigcirc = \bigcirc$, observe that

we can only have two possible multiplication sentences.

$2 \times 3 = 6$ or $2 \times 4 = 8$

We cannot have, say, 3×4 or 2×5, as these products exceed 9.

If we take $2 \times 4 = 8$, then the 9 can only appear in the addition sentence:

$\bigcirc + \bigcirc = 9.$

It cannot be $1 + 8 = 9$, since 8 has already been used, nor can it be $2 + 7$, since 2 has also been used.

Consider $3 + 6 = 9$. Then, we are left with 1, 4, and 5 for the subtraction sentence: $5 - 1 = 4$.

But 4 has also been used.
Hence, $2 \times 4 = 8$ is out.
Let's try $2 \times 3 = 6$.
Then we could have:
$4 + 5 = 9$
$8 - 1 = 7$ or $8 - 7 = 1$
The three mathematical sentences all make use of the digits 1 to 9.
Hence, we could have the following:

$4 + 5 = 9$
$8 - 1 = 7$
$2 \times 3 = 6$

or

$4 + 5 = 9$ (or **$5 + 4 = 9$**)
$8 - 7 = 1$
$2 \times 3 = 6$ (or **$3 \times 2 = 6$**)

Blank

Blank

Blank